PREFACE

Build-your-own projects don't have to be intimidating and confusing. This book is filled with more than 450 do-it-yourself project plans you can order with one phone call. Our project plans are compiled from best-selling projects created by experienced designers. The following pages feature numerous designs for garages, apartment garages, room additions, decks, gazebos, indoor and backyard furniture, children's playhouses, scroll saw, wall art, yard art patterns, and more.

Each garage and building plan includes the following:

- floor plans and elevations
- wall framing and/or details
- material list
- instructions*

Not only do you get the enjoyment of a new addition to your home or yard, but with completion of one of the larger projects you may also significantly increase the value of your property. Each project plan contains a complete list of materials.

* Available with most plans. See plan page for project description.

At the time these project plans were created, every effort has been made to review the contents to ensure accuracy of the information provided herein. However, the reader should check for his or her own assurance and must be responsible for design, selection and use of supplies, materials and actual construction.

Published by: HDA, Inc.
4390 Green Ash Drive
St. Louis, MO 63045-1219
Phone: (314) 770-2222
Fax: (314) 770-2226

Website: www.designamerica.com

Table of Contents

Current Printing (last digit) 5 4 3 2 1
ISBN 0-934039-59-3

1

DESIGN #PB5-11501
Price Code P3

TREE SEAT

- Easily adjusts to fit most trees
- Complete list of materials
- Step-by-step instructions
- Full-size traceable patterns

DESIGN #PB5-11502
Price Code P3

WISHING WELL

- Size - 4'-0" diameter x 7'-0" high
- Includes authentic bucket, operating windlass and crank handle
- Complete list of materials
- Step-by-step instructions
- Full-size traceable patterns

DESIGN #PB5-11503
Price Code P3

REDWOOD PLANTERS

Planter 1

Planter 2

- Six styles to choose from
- Planter 1 - 32" square x 16" high
  Planter 2 - 36" square x 22" high
- Straight cuts and basic assembly make planters simple to build
- Complete list of materials
- Step-by-step instructions

DESIGN #PB5-11504
Price Code P3

DUMP TRUCK

- Size - 4' x 2'
- For ages four to eight
- Working steering mechanism and dump box
- Complete list of materials
- Step-by-step instructions
- Full-size traceable patterns

DESIGN #PB5-11505
Price Code P3

SLED

- Size - 40" x 15"
- Plans are designed with a removable seat
- Complete list of materials
- Step-by-step instructions
- Full-size traceable patterns

DESIGN #PB5-11506
Price Code P3

CANOPY GLIDER SWING

- Size - 8'-0" x 6'-5" x 8'-0" high
- Seats four adults
- Includes small table with cut-outs for drinks
- Complete list of materials
- Step-by-step instructions
- Full-size traceable patterns

DESIGN #PB5-11507
Price Code P3

PLAY STRUCTURE

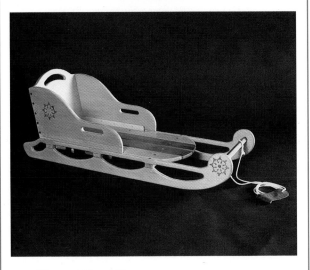

- Size - 6'-0" square x 10'-0" high
- Simple, sturdy post-and-platform construction
- Complete list of materials
- Step-by-step instructions

DESIGN #PB5-11508
Price Code P3

FOLDING ADIRONDACK CHAIR

- Size - 24" x 39" x 37" high
- Good looking and comfortable
- Folds up in one motion
- Complete list of materials
- Step-by-step instructions
- Full-size traceable patterns

DESIGN #PB5-11509
Price Code P3

BIRDHOUSES

- Country birdhouse size - 7" x 9" x 10" high
  Victorian birdhouse size - 8 1/2" x 7" x 18" high
- Complete list of materials
- Step-by-step instructions
- Full-size traceable patterns

DESIGN #PB5-11510
Price Code P3

LIGHTHOUSE

- Size - 22" diameter x 5'-0" high
- Built from one 4' x 8' sheet of plywood
- Complete list of materials
- Step-by-step instructions
- Full-size traceable patterns

DESIGN #PB5-11511
Price Code P3

COASTER CAR

- Size - 62" x 20" x 27 1/2" high
- Safety conscious design features sleek styling, a simple steering mechanism and a convenient hand brake
- Complete list of materials
- Step-by-step instructions
- Full-size traceable patterns

DESIGN #PB5-11512
Price Code P3

SMALL WISHING WELL

- Size - 27" diameter x 40" high
- Perfect addition to any garden
- Complete list of materials
- Step-by-step instructions
- Full-size traceable patterns

DESIGN #PB5-11513
Price Code P3

WHEELBARROW PLANTER

- Size - 40" x 10" x 15" high
- Wheel turns to move planter easily
- Complete list of materials
- Step-by-step instructions
- Full-size traceable patterns

DESIGN #PB5-11514
Price Code P3

WATER PUMP

- Size - 14" square x 44" high
- Designed for use with submersible pump
- Complete list of materials
- Step-by-step instructions
- Full-size traceable patterns

DESIGN #PB5-11515
Price Code P3

PLAYHOUSE

- Size - 6' x 6' x 6' high
- Provides fun and creativity
- Simple, sturdy construction
- Complete list of materials
- Step-by-step instructions

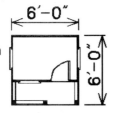

DESIGN #PB5-11516
Price Code P3

WATER WHEEL

- Size - 4' x 3' x 4' high
- Submersible pump keeps water circulating and wheel turning
- Complete list of materials
- Step-by-step instructions
- Full-size traceable patterns

DESIGN #PB5-11520
Price Code P3

BIRDHOUSE ASSORTMENT

- Seven plans: four houses and three feeders
- Projects require only standard hand tools and inexpensive materials
- Traceable pieces
- Complete list of materials
- Step-by-step instructions

DESIGN #PB5-11521
Price Code P3

OCTAGON TABLE SET

- Size - table measures 55" across x 30" tall
- Seats eight or more on combination of two-seat benches and single-seat stools
- Complete list of materials
- Step-by-step instructions

DESIGN #PB5-11522
Price Code P3

PLANTER BENCH

- Size - benches measure 36" long x 15" wide
- Size - planter boxes measure 20 1/2" square x 17" tall
- Modular construction allows builder to configure as preferred
- Complete list of materials
- Step-by-step instructions

DESIGN #PB5-11523
Price Code P3

PORCH ROCKER

- Size - 42" tall x 24 1/2" wide x 28" deep
- Made from standard redwood lumber
- Features mostly straight cuts with full-size patterns for the curved cuts
- Complete list of materials
- Step-by-step instructions

PORCH SWING

- Size - 60" long as pictured, but length may be adjusted
- A handsome and comfortable addition to any porch or patio
- Complete list of materials
- Step-by-step instructions

TWIN-SEATER

- Size - 60" long x 25" deep x 35" tall
- Classic outdoor design
- Complete list of materials
- Step by step instructions

ADIRONDACK QUARTET

- Four easy-to-build Adirondack projects
- Complete list of materials
- Step-by-step instructions

BACKYARD

LEISURE BENCH WITH TABLE

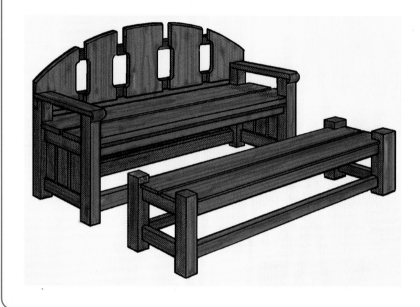

- Bench size - 60" x 20" x 36" high
- Table size - 48" x 20" x 18" high
- Enhance your garden, patio or deck
- Complements any outdoor setting
- Complete list of materials
- Step-by-step instructions

ALL PURPOSE BENCH

- Size - 72" x 20" x 36" high
- Enhance your garden, patio or deck
- Complements any setting
- Complete list of materials
- Step-by-step instructions

DESIGN #PB5-11008
Price Code P3

TWO CUPOLAS

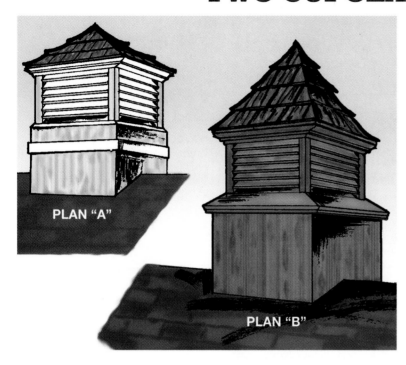

PLAN "A"

PLAN "B"

- Sizes -
  Plan A: 30" x 30" x 40" high
  Plan B: 33" x 33" x 60" high
- A decorative finishing touch for any structure
- Easy to build
- Complete list of materials
- Step-by-step instructions

DESIGN #PB5-11519
Price Code P3

TRELLIS PROJECTS

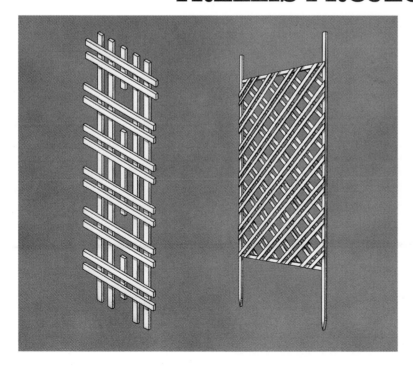

- Fifteen designs to choose from
- Each trellis design adapts easily to fit your landscape and gardening needs
- Complete list of materials
- Step-by-step instructions

DOGHOUSES

- Two popular sizes -
  24" x 36" x 24" high
  32" x 46" x 36" high
- Attractive gable and gambrel roof styles
- Wood cutting diagrams to help you cut cost
- Complete list of materials
- Step-by-step instructions

BIRD HOUSES AND FEEDER

- Three popular sizes and styles
- Martin house -
  26" x 22 1/2" x 26" high
- Perfect for patio or backyard
- Designed for easy maintenance
- Complete list of materials
- Step-by-step instructions

MULTI-LEVEL JUNGLE GYM

- Size - 8' x 8' x 10' high
- Multi-level platforms create a unique play structure
- Outdoor fun for children of all ages
- Complete list of materials
- Step-by-step instructions

BACKYARD

DESIGN #PB5-11011
Price Code P3

SWING SET JUNGLE GYM

- Size - 14' x 13' x 7'-6" high
- Designed with versatility in mind
- Simple construction for easy assembly
- Plenty of outdoor enjoyment for everyone in the family
- Complete list of materials
- Step-by-step instructions

PICNIC BENCH AND TABLE

- Table size - 6'-0" x 5'-2"
- Bench size - 6'-0" x 2'-7"
- Converts from table to bench
- Wood cutting diagrams to help you cut cost
- Sturdy construction
- Complete list of materials
- Step-by-step instructions

PATIO FURNITURE - 3 PIECE SET

- Lounge seat - 63" x 32" x 31" high
- Ideal for patio or deck
- Convenient for outdoor entertaining
- Complete list of materials
- Step-by-step instructions

DESIGN #PB5-11003
Price Code P3

PICNIC TABLES

- Two popular styles -
  Rectangle - 72" x 60" x 30" high
  Octagon - 56" x 56" x 30" high
- Ideal for outdoor entertaining and backyard barbeques
- Complete list of materials
- Step-by-step instructions

DESIGN #PB5-11007
Price Code P3

FENCES AND GATES - 9 DESIGNS

- Nine popular designs to select from
- Ideas for security, privacy and beauty
- From wood framing to chain link fencing
- Guides to help you estimate, buy and build
- Complete list of materials
- Step-by-step instructions

ENTRANCE ARBORS

- Four designs to choose from
- Each arbor design adapts easily to fit your landscape needs
- Complete list of materials
- Step-by-step instructions

LANDSCAPE ARBORS

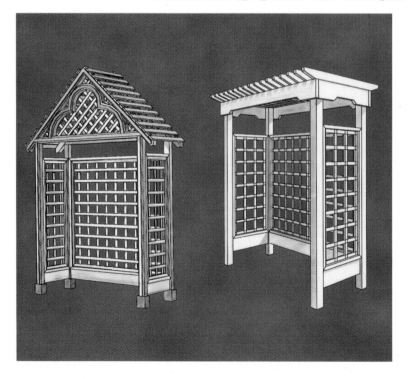

- Four designs to choose from
- Perfect for outdoor garden
- Complete list of materials
- Step-by-step instructions

DESIGN #PB5-11010
Price Code P3

PVC OUTDOOR FURNITURE

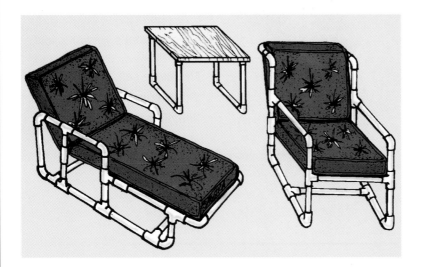

- Perfect for patio or deck
- Designed for easy maintenance
- Very practical and unique
- Simple construction using plastic pipe to build this chair and chaise lounge
- Complete list of materials
- Step-by-step instructions

DESIGN #PB5-11012
Price Code P3

GARDEN SWING WITH CANOPY

- Canopy size - 12'-0" x 5'-0" x 7'-6" high
- Bench size - 6'-0" long
- Attractive design features a sun screen canopy
- Perfect for enjoying the outdoors in style
- Complete list of materials
- Step-by-step instructions

ADIRONDACK CHAIR

- Size - 66" x 27" x 40" high
- A project that's very practical and unique
- Two piece set
- Sturdy construction
- Complete list of materials
- Step-by-step instructions

PORCH SWING

- Size - 72" x 24" x 26" high
- Ideal for attaching to porch or any outdoor structure
- Attractive and sturdy design
- Complete list of materials
- Step-by-step instructions

BUNK BEDS

- Bed size - 3'-5" x 7'-1" x 5'-4" high
- Mattress size - 39" x 75"
- This bunk bed design is both versatile and durable
- Great for growing family or overnight guests
- Complete list of materials
- Step-by-step instructions

INDOOR

GUN/CURIO CABINET

- Size - 40" x 16" x 75" high
- Elegant and traditional in design
- Gun cabinet will hold 6 guns up to 52" long with ample storage below
- Curio cabinet will hold your cherished items on adjustable shelves and also offer plenty of storage in lower cabinet
- Complete list of materials
- Step-by-step instructions

DESIGN #PB5-16517
Price Code P3

SEWING CABINET

- Size - 36" long x 20" wide x 31" tall when closed
- Tabletop is 72" long x 20" wide
- Room for sewing machine, notions, fabric and more
- Complete list of materials
- Step-by-step instructions

DESIGN #PB5-16518
Price Code P3

SPACE-SAVER WORKBENCH

- Size - 72" long x 34" deep x 74" tall when open
- Folds to 72" long x 13" deep x 34" tall when closed
- Full-size workbench plus space for built-in fluorescent light and plenty of storage shelves
- Complete list of materials
- Step-by-step instructions

WET BAR

- Size - 8' x 6' x 3'-6" high
- Attractive serving bar perfect for any room
- Plenty of storage area
- Ideal design for entertaining
- Complete list of materials
- Step-by-step instructions

INDOOR

WORK BENCH WITH CART

- Table size - 70" x 29" x 39" high
- Cart size - 24" x 23" x 36" high
- Practical work bench has a very unique feature . . . a mobile tool caddy that rolls out from under the work bench for added workspace
- Perfect for storing tools and enough work space to handle larger projects
- Complete list of materials
- Step-by-step instructions

ROCKING CRADLE

- Size - 40" x 24" x 35" high
- Complements any furniture setting
- No need to custom order - 18" x 36" standard mattress will fit this attractive cradle and makes decorating easy
- Complete list of materials
- Step-by-step instructions

DESIGN #PB5-16519
Price Code P3

ENTERTAINMENT ARMOIRE

- Size - 70" tall x 39" wide x 23" deep
- Armoire holds 27-inch TV, VCR, stereo equipment and more
- Complete list of materials
- Step-by-step instructions

DESIGN #PB5-16520
Price Code P3

CRAFTSMAN BOOKCASE

- Size - 60" tall x 36" wide x 12" deep
- Features tempered glass doors and three shelves
- Complete list of materials
- Step-by-step instructions

DESIGN #PB5-16521
Price Code P3

GUN CABINET

- Size - 32" wide x 18" deep x 76" tall
- Cabinet holds seven guns
- Both upper and lower compartments lock
- Complete list of materials
- Step-by-step instructions

DESIGN #PB5-16522
Price Code P3

CORNER CABINET

- Size - 72" tall x 27" across the front x 23 1/2" deep on the two sides
- Display space above with large cabinet below
- Complete list of materials
- Step-by-step instructions

DESIGN #PB5-16523
Price Code P3

ROLL-TOP DESK

- Size - 43" tall x 50" long x 28" deep
- Timeless pigeon-hole design
- Nine drawers, two draw boards, sixteen nooks and a pull-down cover
- Complete list of materials
- Step-by-step instructions

DESIGN #PB5-16524
Price Code P3

LAWYER'S BOOKCASE

- Size - 5' tall x 4' wide x 1' deep
- Glass doors protect prized books and collectibles
- Complete list of materials
- Step-by-step instructions

DESIGN #PB5-16525
Price Code P3

CURIO CABINET

- Size - 72" tall x 35" wide x 15" deep
- Height adjustable tempered-glass shelves and elegant glass doors
- Interior lighting showcases precious collectibles
- Complete list of materials
- Step-by-step instructions

DESIGN #PB5-16526
Price Code P3

BLANKET CHEST

- Size - 47" long x 20" deep x 20" tall
- Quick and easy project
- Oak and oak plywood, but pine can be substituted
- Complete list of materials
- Step-by-step instructions

DESIGN #PB5-16527
Price Code P3

CHILD'S ROCKER

- Size - 25" tall x 21" long
- Extra safe and sturdy, with no sharp points or edges
- Made of oak and oak dowels
- Traceable pieces
- Complete list of materials
- Step-by-step instructions

DESIGN #PB5-16528
Price Code P3

LINEN CLOSET

- Size - 68" tall x 29" wide x 14" deep
- Big enough for household towels, linens and bath accessories
- Complete list of materials
- Step-by-step instructions

DESIGN #PB5-16529
Price Code P3

PRECISION TOOL CHEST

- Size - 24" long x 12" deep x 20" tall
- Felt-lined drawers, rubber feet and brass hardware
- Thirteen drawers plus large storage compartment
- Complete list of materials
- Step-by-step instructions

DESIGN #PB5-16530
Price Code P3

JEWELRY & LINGERIE CHEST

- Size - 39" tall x 19" wide x 15" deep
- Mahogany, with porcelain knobs and felt-lined drawers
- Mostly straight cuts makes this an easy project
- Complete list of materials
- Step-by-step instructions

DESIGN #PB5-16501
Price Code P3

ROCKING HORSE

- Size - 32" x 12" x 26" high
- Safe and durable, all parts cut from one piece of 1' x 12' pine
- Complete list of materials
- Step-by-step instructions
- Full-size traceable patterns

DESIGN #PB5-16502
Price Code P3

CAR BED

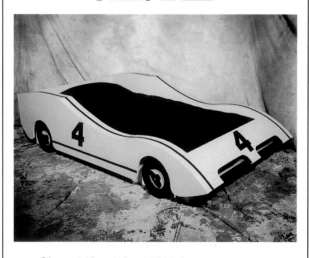

- Size - 86" x 48" x 20" high
- Sturdy construction fits either junior or twin mattresses
- Complete list of materials
- Step-by-step instructions
- Full-size traceable patterns

DESIGN #PB5-16503
Price Code P3

CEDAR CHEST

- Size - 48" x 20" x 20" high
- A classic style that's both handsome and sturdy
- Complete list of materials
- Step-by-step instructions
- Full-size traceable patterns

DESIGN #PB5-16504
Price Code P3

HERITAGE CRADLE

- Size - 33" x 27" x 27" high
- Beautiful, sturdy construction with limited rocking motion
- Complete list of materials
- Step-by-step instructions
- Full-size traceable patterns

INDOOR

DESIGN #PB5-16505
Price Code P3

TWO-DOOR ICE BOX

- Size - 24" x 16" x 38" high
- Authentic reproduction made with oak plywood and brass hardware
- Complete list of materials
- Step-by-step instructions

DESIGN #PB5-16506
Price Code P3

PONY ROCKER

- Size - 44" x 12" x 25" high
- A classic design with the mane and tail made from yarn and scrap leather for the ears
- Complete list of materials
- Step-by-step instructions
- Full-size traceable patterns

DESIGN #PB5-16507
Price Code P3

DEER PLANTER TRIO

- Size - 16" high, 24" high, 32" high
- Simple design for indoor or outdoor use
- Complete list of materials
- Step-by-step instructions
- Full-size traceable patterns

DESIGN #PB5-16508
Price Code P3

BLANKET CHEST AND SEAT

- Size - 48" x 19" x 36" high
- Simple country styling with a hinged bench seat
- Complete list of materials
- Step-by-step instructions

DESIGN #PB5-16509
Price Code P3

STORAGE BINS

- Size - 19" x 12" x 40" high
- Wire mesh allows air to circulate
- Two pull-out bins and a shelf
- Complete list of materials
- Step-by-step instructions

DESIGN #PB5-16510
Price Code P3

ROCKING DINOSAUR

- Size - 45" x 12" x 36" high
- A sweet disposition makes this dinosaur rocker a favorite with kids
- "Fossils" for rockers are sturdy, yet whimsical
- Complete list of materials
- Step-by-step instructions
- Full-size traceable patterns

INDOOR

DESIGN #PB5-16511
Price Code P3

TABLE-TOP SLEIGH

- Size - 27" x 11" x 15" high
- Great holiday gift
- Complete list of materials
- Step-by-step instructions
- Full-size traceable patterns

Note: For Reindeer Planter, see Design #PB5-16507 on page 24

DESIGN #PB5-16512
Price Code P3

FUTON SOFABED

- Size - 86" x 36" x 33" high
- Folds up or down in one smooth motion
- Fits full-size mattress
- Complete list of materials
- Step-by-step instructions

DESIGN #PB5-16513
Price Code P3

CURIO TABLE

- Size - 38" x 24" x 17" high
- Top drawer provides four square feet of display space and is protected with glass
- Complete list of materials
- Step-by-step instructions

DESIGN #PB5-16514
Price Code P3

CORNER T.V. CABINET

- Size - 29" deep x 47" high
- Fits up to a 27" T.V. and features a shelf for a VCR and cable box
- Complete list of materials
- Step-by-step instructions

DESIGN #PB5-16515
Price Code P3

WOODWORKING BENCH

- Size - 60" x 26" x 36" high
- All straight cuts and simple construction techniques
- Complete list of materials
- Step-by-step instructions

DESIGN #PB5-16516
Price Code P3

HUMIDOR

- Size - 13" x 12" x 6" high
- Elegant accessory for cigar smokers
- Complete list of materials
- Step-by-step instructions

SALT BOX STORAGE SHEDS

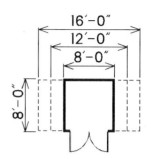

- Three popular sizes -
  8' wide x 8' deep
  12' wide x 8' deep
  16' wide x 8' deep
- Wood floor on gravel base or concrete floor
- Height floor to peak - 8'-2"

- Front wall height - 7'-0"
- 6'-0" x 6'-5" double-door for easy access
- Complete list of materials
- Step-by-step instructions

GABLE STORAGE SHEDS

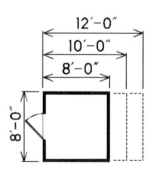

- Three popular sizes -
  8' wide x 8' deep
  8' wide x 10' deep
  8' wide x 12' deep
- Wood floor on concrete footings
- Height floor to peak - 9'-1"

- Wall height - 6'-7"
- Circle-top window adds interest and light
- Complete list of materials
- Step-by-step instructions

SHEDS

YARD BARNS

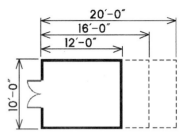

- Three popular sizes -
  10' wide x 12' deep
  10' wide x 16' deep
  10' wide x 20' deep
- Wood floor on 4" x 4" runners
- Height floor to peak - 8'-4 1/2"

- Ceiling height - 6'-4"
- 4'-0" x 6'-4" double-door for easy access
- Ample storage area for lawn or garden equipment
- Complete list of materials
- Step-by-step instructions

MINI BARNS

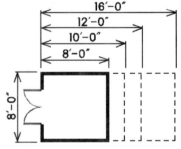

- Four popular sizes -
  8' wide x 8' deep
  8' wide x 10' deep
  8' wide x 12' deep
  8' wide x 16' deep
- Wood floor on 4" x 4" runners
- Height floor to peak - 7'-6"

- Ceiling height - 6'-0"
- 4'-0" x 6'-0" double-door for easy access
- Perfect for storage of lawn and garden equipment
- Attractive styling for any backyard
- Complete list of materials
- Step-by-step instructions

GABLE STORAGE SHEDS

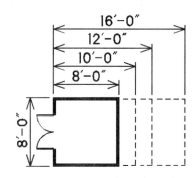

- Four popular sizes -
  8' wide x 8' deep
  8' wide x 10' deep
  8' wide x 12' deep
  8' wide x 16' deep
- Wood floor on 4" x 4" runners
- Height floor to peak - 8'-4 1/2"

- Ceiling height - 7'-0"
- 4'-0" x 6'-5" double-door for easy access
- Economical and easy to build shed
- Complete list of materials
- Step-by-step instructions

GABLE STORAGE SHEDS

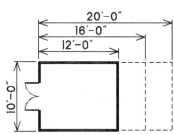

- Three popular sizes -
  10' wide x 12' deep
  10' wide x 16' deep
  10' wide x 20' deep
- Wood floor on 4" x 4" runners
- Height floor to peak - 8'-8 1/2"

- Ceiling height - 7'-0"
- 4'-0" x 6'-4" double-door for easy access
- Complete list of materials
- Step-by-step instructions

SHEDS

GARDEN SHED

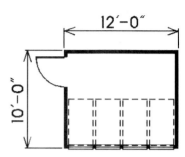

- Size - 12' wide x 10' deep
- Wood floor on gravel base
- Height floor to peak - 9'-9"
- Rear wall height - 7'-1 1/2"

- Features skylight windows for optimal plant growth
- Ample room for tool and lawn equipment storage

- Complete list of materials
- Step-by-step instructions

GARDEN SHED

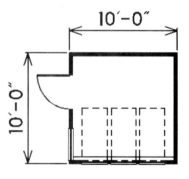

- Size - 10' wide x 10' deep
- Wood floor on 4" x 4" runners
- Height floor to peak - 11'-3 1/2"
- Left wall height - 8'-0"
- Wonderful complement to any backyard

- Perfect space for lawn equipment or plants and flowers
- Plenty of windows for gardening year-round
- Complete list of materials
- Step-by-step instructions

CONVENIENCE SHED

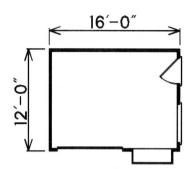

- Size - 16' wide x 12' deep
- Concrete floor
- Height floor to peak - 12'-4 1/2"
- Ceiling height - 8'-0"
- 8'-0" x 7'-0" overhead door

- Ideal for lawn equipment or small boat storage
- Oversized windows brighten interior
- Complete list of materials
- Step-by-step instructions

BARN STORAGE SHED WITH OVERHEAD DOOR

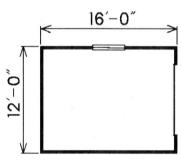

- Size - 12' wide x 16' deep
- Concrete floor
- Height floor to peak - 12'-5"

- Ceiling height - 8'-0"
- 8'-0" x 7'-0" overhead door for easy entry with large equipment
- Side windows add light to interior

- Complete list of materials
- Step-by-step instructions

SHEDS

BARN STORAGE SHEDS WITH LOFT

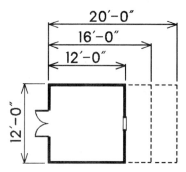

- Three popular sizes -
  12' wide x 12' deep
  12' wide x 16' deep
  12' wide x 20' deep
- Wood floor on concrete pier foundation or concrete floor

- Height floor to peak - 12'-10"
- Ceiling height - 7'-4"
- 4'-0" x 6'-8" double-door for easy access
- Complete list of materials
- Step-by-step instructions

GARDEN SHEDS WITH CLERESTORY

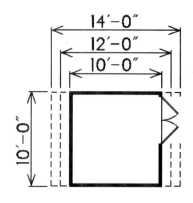

- Three popular sizes -
  10' wide x 10' deep
  12' wide x 10' deep
  14' wide x 10' deep
- Wood floor on 4" x 6" runners

- Height floor to peak - 10'-11"
- Rear wall height - 7'-3"
- 5'-0" x 6'-9" double-door for easy access

- Clerestory windows for added light
- Complete list of materials
- Step-by-step instructions

GARDEN SHED WITH PORCH

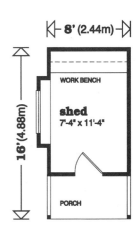

8' (2.44m)

16' (4.88m)

WORK BENCH

shed
7'-4" x 11'-4"

PORCH

- Size - 8' x 16'
- Building height -11'-16"
- Ceiling height - 8'-0"
- Roof pitch - 7/12
- Covered front porch
- Handy built-in work bench
- Complete list of materials
- Plans are printed on 8 1/2" x 11" pages

ECONO BARN

- Size - 9'-2" x 7'-9"
- Building height - 8'-0"
- Ceiling height - 4'-9"
- Concrete floor
- Double-door for easy access
- Complete list of materials
- Plans are printed on 8 1/2" x 11" pages

SHEDS

DESIGN #PB5-12018
Price Code P5

STORAGE SHED WITH LOG BIN

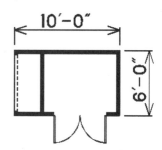

- Size - 10' wide x 6' deep
- Wood floor on gravel base
- Height floor to peak - 9'-7"
- Ceiling height - 6'-7"
- 5'-0" x 6'-9" double-door for easy access
- Log storage area - 2'-6" x 6'-0"
- Complete list of materials
- Step-by-step instructions

DESIGN #PB5-12506
Price Code P4

GAMBREL SHED

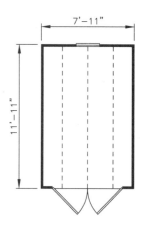

- Size - 12' x 8'
- Building height - 8'-0"
- Ceiling height - 6'-0"
- Wood floor on concrete pier foundation or concrete floor
- Complete list of materials
- Plans come on printed 8 1/2" x 11" pages

GREENHOUSE

- Size - 12' wide x 8' deep
- Gravel floor with concrete foundation wall
- Height foundation to peak - 8'-3"
- An attractive addition to any yard
- Store lawn and garden tools right at hand
- Complete list of materials
- Step-by-step instructions

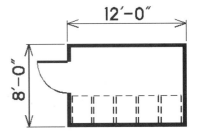

SHEDS

UTILITY SHED

- Three popular sizes -
  12' wide x 8' deep
  14' wide x 10' deep
  16' wide x 12' deep
- Wood floor on 4" x 4" runners or concrete floor
- Height floor to peak - 11'-6"
- Ceiling height - 8'-0"
- Shed has room for tools and lawn equipment
- 5'-0" x 6'-8" double-door for easy access
- Complete list of materials
- Step-by-step instructions

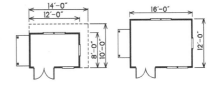

POOL CABANA

- Size - 12' x 20'
- Building height - 11'-6"
- Ceiling height - 8'-0"
- Roof pitch - 7/12
- Slab foundation

- Charming cottage-style has convenient bath, towel storage and a dressing area
- Complete list of materials
- Plans are printed on 8 1/2" x 11" pages

RUSTIC POOL CABANA

- Size – 20' x 12'
- Building height - 11'-6"
- Ceiling height - 8'-0"
- Roof pitch - 7/12
- Slab foundation

- Rustic design creates a cabin feel
- Pool cabana includes plenty of storage, a full bath and a changing room
- Complete list of materials
- Plans are printed on 8 1/2" x 11" pages

SUMMER PAVILION

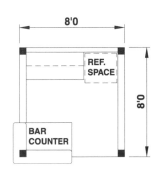

- Size - 8' x 8'
- Building height - 13'-0"
- Summer pavilion would be perfect for outdoor entertaining and features built-in shelves, bar counter and space for a refridgerator

- Complete list of materials
- Plans are printed on 8 1/2" x 11" pages

SHEDS

YARD BARN WITH LOFT STORAGE

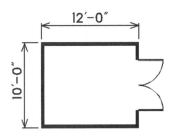

- Size - 10' wide x 12' deep
- Wood floor on 4" x 4" runners
- Height floor to peak - 10'-7"
- Ceiling height - 6'-11"
- 6'-0" x 6'-2" double-door for easy access

- Loft provides additional storage area
- Attractive styling suitable for yard
- Complete list of materials
- Step-by-step instructions

DELUXE CABANA

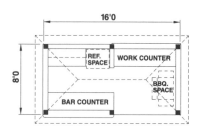

- Size - 11'-0" wide x 13'-6" deep
- Concrete floor
- Height floor to peak - 11'-7"
- Ceiling height - 8'-0"
- Unique roof design with skylight

- Convenient dressing room and servicing area
- Perfect storage for poolside furniture and equipment
- Complete list of materials
- Step-by-step instructions

SUMMER PAVILION

- Size - 16' x 8'
- Building height - 13'-0"
- Convenient space for outdoor entertaining features outdoor barbecue area, refrigerator area and eating and preparation counters

- Complete list of materials
- Plans are printed on 8 1/2" x 11" pages

SALTBOX STORAGE SHED

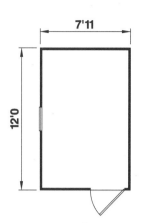

- Size - 7'-11" x 12'-0"
- Building height - 9'-0"
- Ceiling height - 6'-6"
- Narrow design allows this shed to fit most anywhere

- Roof pitch - 4/12
- Barnyard-style door
- Complete list of materials
- Plans are printed on 8 1/2" x 11" pages

SHEDS

DESIGN #PB5-12021
Price Code P5

SALT BOX STORAGE SHED

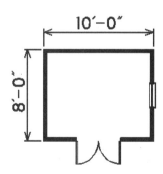

- Size - 10' wide x 8' deep
- Wood floor on 4" x 4" runners
- Height floor to peak - 9'-6"
- Front wall height - 8'-0"

- 4'-0" x 6'-8" double-door for easy access
- Window adds light to space
- Complete list of materials
- Step-by-step instructions

PLAYHOUSE

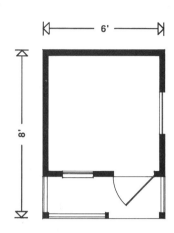

- Size - 6' x 8'
- Building height - 8'-6"
- Ceiling height - 4'-8"
- Roof pitch - 10/12
- Wood floor on concrete piers

- 2' deep porch
- Charming cottage makes an ideal children's playhouse
- Petite covered porch adds a nice touch
- Complete list of materials
- Plans are printed on 8 1/2" x 11" pages

RUSTIC PLAYHOUSE

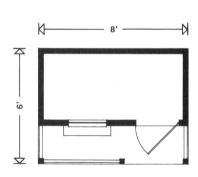

- Size - 8' x 6'
- Building height - 8'-6"
- Ceiling height - 4'-9"
- Roof pitch - 10/12
- 2' deep porch

- Wood floor on concrete blocks
- Charming covered porch
- Complete list of materials
- Plans are printed on 8 1/2" x 11" pages

DESIGN #PB5-12006
Price Code P4

CHILDREN'S PLAYHOUSE

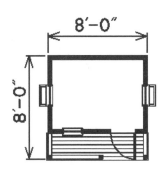

- Size - 8' wide x 8' deep
- Wood floor on 4" x 4" runners
- Height floor to peak - 9'-2"
- Ceiling height - 6'-1"
- 2' deep porch
- Attractive window boxes
- Includes operable windows
- Complete list of materials
- Step-by-step instructions

SHEDS

DESIGN #PB5-12019
Price Code P4

CHILDREN'S PLAYHOUSE

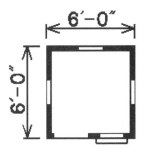

- Size - 6' wide x 6' deep
- Wood floor on gravel base
- Height floor to peak - 7'-2"
- Wall height - 4'-4"
- Plenty of windows brighten interior
- Gabled doorway and window box add interest
- Attractive Victorian style
- Complete list of materials
- Step-by-step instructions

STORAGE SHED WITH PLAYHOUSE LOFT

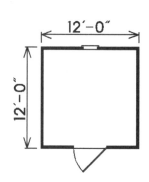

- Size - 12' wide x 12' deep with 2'-8" deep balcony
- Wood floor on concrete piers or concrete floor
- Height floor to peak - 14'-1"

- Ceiling height - 7'-4"
- 4'-0" x 6'-10" door
- Loft above can be used as playhouse for children

- Loft features ladder for easy access
- Complete list of materials
- Step-by-step instructions

GABLE STORAGE SHED/PLAYHOUSE

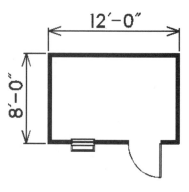

- Size - 12' wide x 8' deep
- Wood floor on 4" x 4" runners
- Height floor to peak - 10'-5"
- Ceiling height - 8'-0"
- 3'-0" x 6'-8" Dutch door

- Perfect for storage or a playhouse for children
- Shutters and window box create a charming facade
- Complete list of materials
- Step-by-step instructions

GARDEN SHED WITH PLAYHOUSE

16' (4.88m)

12' (3.66m)

WORK BENCH

garden storage
7'4" x 11'4"

playhouse
7'8" x 7'4"

COVERED AREA

SHEDS

- Size - 16'-0" x 12'-0"
- Building height - 13'-0"
- Ceiling heights - 7'-0" and 8'-0"
- Roof pitch - 12/12
- Charming country cottage style
- Wood floor on concrete piers or concrete floor
- Garden shed with playhouse combines efficiency with fun
- Complete list of materials
- Plans are printed on 8 1/2" x 11" pages

WHIPPLEWOOD COTTAGE/PLAYHOUSE

8'0

8'0

up   up   VAULT   VAULT

VAULT   VAULT

VAULT   VAULT

PORCH

- Size - 8' x 8'
- Building height - 8'-0"
- Ceiling height - 6'-0"
- Roof pitch - 10/12 and 4/12
- Wood floor on concrete piers or concrete floor
- Victorian details add flair to this playhouse
- Complete list of materials
- Plans are printed on 8 1/2" x 11" pages

STORAGE SHED

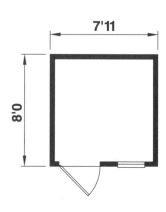

7'11

8'0

- Size - 7'-11" x 8'-0"
- Building height - 8'-6"
- Ceiling height - 6'-6"
- Roof pitch - 4/12

- Ample storage space for lawn or garden equipment
- Complete list of materials
- Plans are printed on 8 1/2" x 11" pages

SALTBOX STORAGE SHED

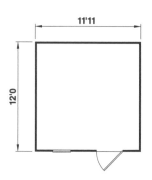

11'11

12'0

- Size - 11'-11" x 12'-0"
- Building height - 9'-0"
- Ceiling height - 6'-6"
- Roof pitch - 4/12

- Wood floor on concrete piers or concrete floor
- Easily accommodates large yard equipment

- Shed can easily be converted to a workshop
- Complete list of materials
- Plans are printed on 8 1/2" x 11" pages

YARD AND GARDEN SHED

- Three popular sizes -
  8' wide x 12' deep
  10' wide x 14' deep
  12' wide x 16' deep

- Wood floor on 4" x 4" runners or concrete floor

- Height floor to peak - 11'-6"

- Ceiling height - 8'-0"

- 3' x 9' side storage with over-hang

- 5'-0" x 6'-8" double-door

- Complete list of materials

- Step-by-step instructions

SHEDS

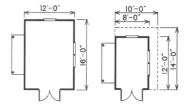

SALTBOX STORAGE SHED

- Three popular sizes-
  12' wide x 8' deep
  14' wide x 10' deep
  16' wide x 12' deep

- Wood floor on 4" x 4" runners or concrete floor

- Height floor to peak - 12'-6"

- Ceiling height - 8'-0"

- An attractive addition to any backyard

- 5'-0" x 6'-8" double-door

- Complete list of materials

- Step-by-step instructions

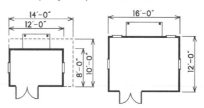

DESIGN #PB5-12518
Price Code P4

STORAGE SHED

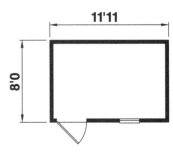

11'11

8'0

- Size 11'-11" x 8'-0"
- Building height - 8'-6"
- Ceiling height - 6'-6"
- Roof pitch - 4/12

- Wood floor on concrete piers or concrete floor
- Could easily be converted to a children's playhouse
- Complete list of materials
- Plans are printed on 8 1/2" x 11" pages

DESIGN #PB5-12519
Price Code P4

STORAGE SHED

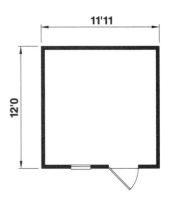

11'11

12'0

- Size - 11'-11" x 12'-0"
- Building height - 9'-0"
- Ceiling height - 6'-6"
- Roof pitch - 4/12

- Wood floor on piers or concrete floor
- Interior brightened by front window
- Complete list of materials

GABLE STORAGE SHED WITH CUPOLA

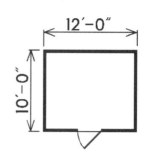

12'-0"

10'-0"

- Size - 12' wide x 10' deep
- Wood floor on concrete piers or concrete floor
- Height floor to peak - 9'-8"
- Ceiling height - 7'-4"

- 3'-0" x 6'-8" door
- Made of cedar plywood with battens
- Complete list of materials
- Step-by-step instructions

SLANT ROOF SHED

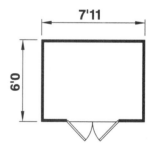

7'11

6'0

- Size - 7'-11" x 6'-0"
- Building height - 8'-0"
- Front wall height - 7'-6"
- Roof pitch - 4/12

- Wood floor on concrete piers or concrete floor
- Wide double-doors allow for easy storage
- Complete list of materials
- Plans are printed on 8 1/2" x 11" pages

DESIGN #PB5-12521
Price Code P4

SALTBOX STORAGE SHED

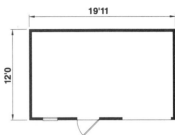

19'11

12'0

- Size - 19'-11" x 12'-0"
- Building height - 9'-0"
- Ceiling height - 6'-6"
- Roof pitch - 4/12

- Wood floor on concrete piers or concrete floor
- Complete list of materials
- Plans are printed on 8 1/2" x 11" pages

DESIGN #PB5-12013
Price Code P4

PLAYHOUSE/STORAGE SHED

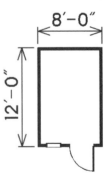

8'-0"

12'-0"

- Size - 8' wide x 12' deep
- Height floor to peak - 10'-6"
- Ceiling height - 7'-0"
- Wood floor on concrete piers or concrete floor
- 3'-0" x 6'-0" door

- Quaint chalet design
- Ideal playhouse in summer
- Storage shed in the off-season
- Complete list of materials
- Step-by-step instructions

BARN STORAGE SHEDS

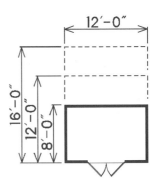

- Three popular sizes -
  12' wide x 8' deep
  12' wide x 12' deep
  12' wide x 16' deep
- Wood floor on concrete pier foundation or concrete floor
- Height floor to peak - 9'-10"

- Ceiling height - 7'-10"
- 5'-6" x 6'-8" double-door
- Gambrel roof design
- Complete list of materials
- Step-by-step instructions

SHEDS

MINI BARN STORAGE SHEDS

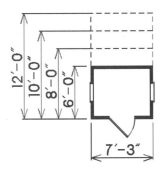

- Four popular sizes -
  7'-3" wide x 6' deep
  7'-3" wide x 8' deep
  7'-3" wide x 10' deep
  7'-3" wide x 12' deep

- Wood floor on 4" x 6" runners or concrete floor
- Height floor to peak - 9'-0"
- Ceiling height - 7'-4"

- 3'-0" x 6'-8" door
- Attractive styling with gambrel roof
- Complete list of materials
- Step-by-step instructions

2-CAR GARAGE WITH BOAT STORAGE

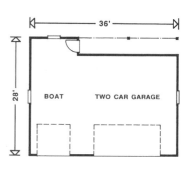

- Size - 36' x 28'
- Building height - 15'-0"
- Ceiling height - 8'-0"
- Attractive gable roof style works well with many home styles

- Roof pitch - 5/12
- Easily accommodates boat or other recreational vehicles
- Complete list of materials

R.V. GARAGE

- Size - 18' x 36'
- Building height - 20'-6"
- Ceiling height - 14'-0"
- Roof pitch - 7/12

- Double windows provide plenty of natural light indoors
- Convenient side and rear entry doors
- Complete list of materials
- Plans are printed on 8 1/2" x 11" pages

3-CAR GARAGE WITH WORKSHOP

32'-0"

28'-0"

Workshop Area

- Size - 32' x 28'
- Building height - 13'-3"
- Roof pitch - 4/12
- Ceiling height - 8'-0"
- 9' x 7' and 16' x 7' overhead doors

- Handy workshop space for hobbies
- Side-entry door provides easy access
- Complete list of materials
- Step-by-step instructions

3-CAR GARAGE/WORKSHOP

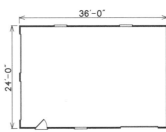

36'-0"

24'-0"

- Size - 24' x 36'
- Building height - 14'-6"
- Ceiling height - 10'-0"
- Roof pitch - 4/12
- Three 9' x 8' overhead doors

- Oversized for storage
- Ideal size for workshop or maintenance building
- Complete list of materials
- Step-by-step instructions

GARAGES

2-CAR GARAGE WITH LOFT

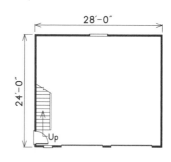

- Size - 28' x 24'
- Building height - 21'-0"
- Ceiling height - 8'-0"
- Roof pitch - 12/12

- Loft ceiling height - 7'-6"
- Two 9' x 7' overhead doors
- Complete list of materials
- Step-by-step instructions

2-CAR GARAGE WITH WORKSHOP & LOFT

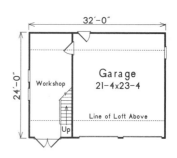

- Size - 32' x 24'
- Building height - 21'-0"
- Roof pitch - 12/12
- Ceiling height - 8'-0"
- Loft ceiling height - 7'-6"

- Two 9' x 7' overhead doors
- Plenty of storage space for workshop or hobby center
- Complete list of materials
- Step-by-step instructions

1-CAR GARAGE
WITH LOFT - GAMBREL ROOF

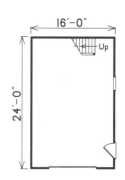

- Size - 16' x 24'
- Building height - 18'-9"
- Roof pitch - 12/6, 6/12
- Ceiling height - 8'-0"

- Loft ceiling height - 6'-7"
- 9' x 7' overhead door
- Ideal loft is perfect for workshop or storage area

- Handy side door
- Complete list of materials
- Step-by-step instructions

2-CAR GARAGE WITH LOFT

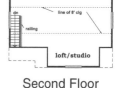

Second Floor

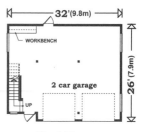

First Floor

- Size - 32' x 26'
- Building height - 23'-0"
- Roof pitch - 12/12
- Ceiling height - 8'-0"
- Two 9' x 7' overhead doors

- Handy workbench with plenty of workspace
- Additional storage available in loft
- Complete list of materials

1-CAR GARAGE WITH R.V. STORAGE

- Size - 30' x 36'
- Building height - 21'-0"
- Ceiling heights - 14'-0" and 9'-0"
- Roof pitch - 7/12

- Easily accessible side and rear entry doors
- Complete list of materials

2-CAR GARAGE WITH R.V. STORAGE

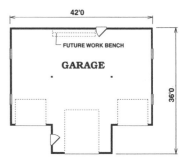

- Size - 42' x 36'
- Building height - 21'-0"
- Ceiling heights - 9'-0" and 14'-0"

- Roof pitch - 7/12
- Offers perfect storage options
- Complete list of materials

2-CAR GARAGE WITH LOFT - GAMBREL ROOF

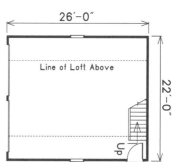

26'-0"

Line of Loft Above

22'-0"

Up

- Size - 22' x 26'
- Building height - 20'-7"
- Roof pitch - 7/12, 12/7
- Ceiling height - 8'-0"

- Loft ceiling height - 7'-4"
- Two 9' x 7' overhead doors
- Complete list of materials
- Step-by-step instructions

2-CAR GARAGE - REVERSE GABLE

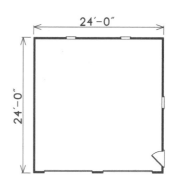

24'-0"

24'-0"

- Size - 24' x 24'
- Building height - 16'-7"
- Roof pitch - 8/12
- Ceiling height - 8'-0"
- Two 9' x 7' overhead doors

- Oversized, appealing design
- Side door is a handy feature
- Complete list of materials
- Step-by-step instructions

GARAGES

DESIGN #PB5-14516
Price Code P9

2-CAR GARAGE WITH LOFT

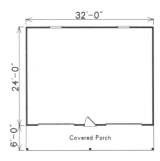

Loft

First Floor

- Size - 28' x 24'
- Building height - 22'-0"
- Roof pitch - 12/12
- Ceiling height - 8'-0"
- Loft ceiling height - 8'-0"
- Two 9' x 7' overhead doors
- Complete list of materials
- Plans are printed on 8 1/2" x 11" pages

DESIGN #PB5-14043
Price Code P7

2 1/2 CAR GARAGE/ROADSIDE STAND

Covered Porch

- Size - 32' x 30'
- Building height - 15'-7"
- Roof pitch - 4/12
- Ceiling height - 10'-0"
- Two 9' x 8' overhead doors
- Excellent for displaying, selling and storing fresh produce
- 6' cantilevered front overhang
- Complete list of materials
- Step-by-step instructions

1-CAR GARAGE

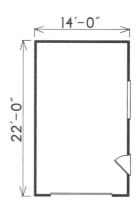

- Size - 14' x 22'
- Building height - 10'-10"
- Roof pitch - 4/12
- Ceiling height - 8'-0"
- 9' x 7' overhead door

- Side window enhances exterior
- Side entry is convenient
- Complete list of materials
- Step-by-step instructions

1-CAR GARAGE - WESTERN STYLE

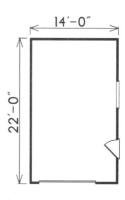

- Size - 14' x 22'
- Building height - 10'-10"
- Roof pitch - 4/12
- Ceiling height - 8'-0"
- 9' x 7' overhead door

- Compact size, perfect for smaller lots
- Efficient side door provides easy access
- Complete list of materials
- Step-by-step instructions

GARAGES

2-CAR GARAGE - GAMBREL ROOF

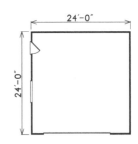

- Size - 24' x 24'
- Building height - 15'-5"
- Roof pitch - 12/8, 4/12
- Ceiling height - 8'-0"

- 16' x 7' overhead door
- Attractive addition to any home
- Complete list of materials
- Step-by-step instructions

2-CAR GARAGE - REVERSE GABLE

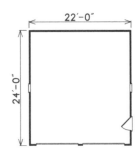

- Size - 22' x 24'
- Building height - 13'-8"
- Roof pitch - 5/12
- Ceiling height - 8'-0"

- Two 9' x 7' overhead doors
- Complete list of materials
- Step-by-step instructions

4-CAR GARAGE WITH OFFICE

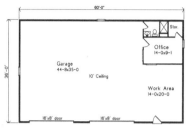

- Size - 60' x 36'
- Building height - 20'-0"
- Roof pitch - 5/12
- Ceiling height - 10'-0"

- Convenient office area with storage is secluded for privacy and includes a half bath nearby
- Two 16' x 8' overhead doors
- Complete list of materials

2-CAR GARAGE

- Size - 24' x 38'
- Building height - 14'-0"
- Roof pitch - 4/12
- Ceiling height - 9'-0"

- 16' x 7' overhead door
- Convenient side entry
- Complete list materials

GARAGES

1-CAR GARAGE WITH COVERED PORCH

- Size - 24' x 22'
- Building height - 13'-0"
- Roof pitch - 5/12
- Ceiling height - 8'-0"
- 9' x 7' overhead door

- Distinctive covered porch provides area for entertaining
- Complete list of materials
- Step-by-step instructions

1-CAR GARAGE

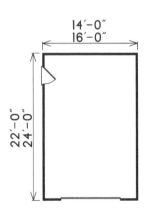

- Four popular sizes -
  14' x 22'   14' x 24'
  16' x 22'   16' x 24'
- Building height - 11'-2"
- Roof pitch - 4/12
- Ceiling height - 8'-0"

- 9' x 7' overhead door
- Sturdy, attractive design
- Complete list of materials
- Step-by-step instructions

GABLED 2-CAR GARAGE

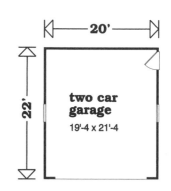

two car garage
19'-4 x 21'-4

20'

22'

- Size - 20' x 22'
- Building height - 13'-0"
- Ceiling height - 8'-0"
- Roof pitch - 5/12

- Convenient side entry door
- Gable adds interest to exterior
- Complete list of materials

GARAGES

3-CAR GARAGE

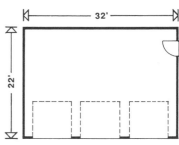

32'

22'

- Size - 32' x 22'
- Building height - 13'-6"
- Ceiling height - 8'-0"
- Roof pitch - 5/12

- Three 9' x 7' overhead doors
- Optional side entry door
- Complete list of windows

3-CAR GARAGE

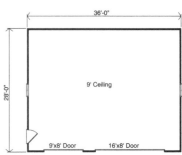

- Size - 36' x 28'
- Building height - 17'-0"
- Roof pitch - 4/12
- Ceiling height - 9'-0"
- 9' x 8' overhead door

- 16' x 8' overhead door
- Versatile style looks good with many different styles of homes
- Complete list of materials

2-CAR GARAGE

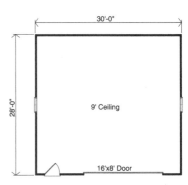

- Size - 30' x 28'
- Building height - 17'-0"
- Roof pitch - 4/12
- Ceiling height - 9'-0"

- 16' x 8' overhead door
- Two side windows brighten interior
- Complete list of materials

Price Code P6

2-CAR ECONOMY GARAGE - HIP ROOF

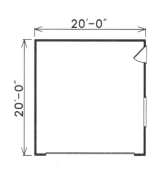

20'-0"

20'-0"

- Size - 20' x 20'
- Building height - 12'-0"
- Roof pitch - 4/12
- Ceiling height - 8'-0"
- 16' x 7' overhead door

- Attractive hip roof design look on any lot
- Extended roof over garage door protects from the weather
- Complete list of materials
- Step-by-step instructions

DESIGN #PB5-14037
Price Code P6

2-CAR ECONOMY GARAGE

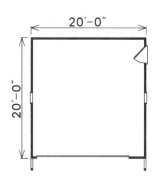

20'-0"

20'-0"

- Size - 20' x 20'
- Building height - 12'-0"
- Roof pitch - 4/12
- Ceiling height - 8'-0"
- 16' x 7' garage door

- Practical and functional
- Convenient side door
- Complete list of materials
- Step-by-step instructions

1-CAR GARAGE

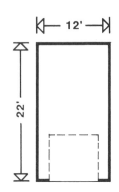

- Size - 12' x 22'
- Building height - 11'-0"
- Ceiling height - 8'-0"

- Roof pitch - 5/12
- Complete list of materials

2-CAR GARAGE WITH LOFT

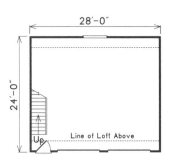

- Size - 28' x 24'
- Building height - 21'-0"
- Roof pitch - 12/12
- Ceiling height - 8'-0"
- Loft ceiling height - 7'-6"

- Two 9' x 7' overhead doors
- Charming dormers add character
- Handy side door accessing stairs to loft
- Complete list of materials

2-CAR ECONOMY GARAGE

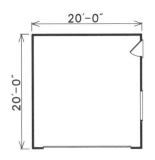

20'-0"

20'-0"

- Size - 20' x 20'
- Building height - 11'-10"
- Roof pitch - 4/12
- Ceiling height - 8'-0"

- 16' x 7' overhead door
- Convenient side door
- Complete list of materials
- Step-by-step instructions

2-CAR GARAGE - REVERSE GABLE

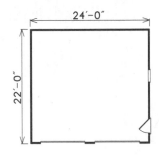

24'-0"

22'-0"

- Size - 24' x 22'
- Building height - 14'-8"
- Roof pitch - 8.5/12, 5/12
- Ceiling height - 8'-0"
- Two 9' x 7' overhead doors

- Roof overhang above garage doors adds custom look
- Handy side door
- Complete list of materials
- Step-by-step instructions

GARAGES

DESIGN #PB5-14004
Price Code P7

2-CAR GARAGE

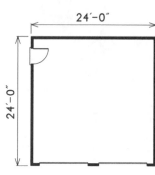

24'-0"

24'-0"

- Size - 24' x 24'
- Building height - 12'-6"
- Roof pitch - 4/12
- Ceiling height - 8'-0"

- Two 9' x 7' overhead doors
- Side entry is efficient and well-designed
- Complete list of materials
- Step-by-step instructions

DESIGN #PB5-14024
Price Code P7

2-CAR GARAGE - WESTERN STYLE

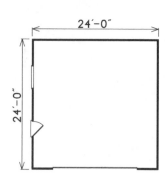

24'-0"

24'-0"

- Size - 24' x 24'
- Building height - 12'-8"
- Roof pitch - 4/12
- Ceiling height - 8'-0"
- 16' x 7' overhead door

- Appealing style with many homes
- Side door and window are functional extras
- Complete list of materials
- Step-by-step instructions

2-CAR GARAGE

- Size - 24' x 30'
- Building height - 15'-0"
- Roof pitch - 4/12
- Ceiling height - 9'-0"

- Two 9' x 7' overhead doors
- Side entry and window brighten interior
- Complete list of materials

GARAGES

2-CAR GARAGE

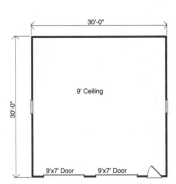

- Size - 30' x 30'
- Building height - 15'-0"
- Roof pitch - 4/12
- Ceiling height - 9'-0"

- Two 9' x 7' overhead doors
- Roomy two-car garage has convenient entry door
- Complete list of materials

2-CAR GARAGE

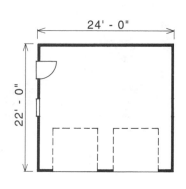

- Size - 24' x 22'
- Building height - 13'-6"
- Ceiling height - 8'-0"

- Roof pitch - 5/12
- Complete list of materials
- Plans are printed on 8 1/2" x 11" pages

2-CAR GARAGE WITH STORAGE

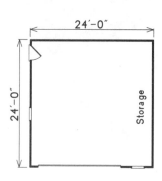

- Size - 24' x 24'
- Building height - 12'-8"
- Roof pitch - 4/12
- Ceiling height - 8'-0"
- 16' x 7' overhead door

- Windows and side door add appeal
- Functional and practical
- Complete list of materials
- Step-by-step instructions

DESIGN #PB5-14527
Price Code P9

5-CAR GARAGE

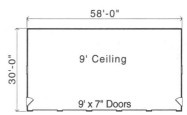

58'-0"

30'-0"

9' Ceiling

9' x 7" Doors

- Size - 58' x 30'
- Building height - 15'-0"
- Roof pitch - 4/12
- Ceiling height - 9'-0"

- Five 9' x 7' overhead doors
- Two convenient side doors allow for easy access
- Complete list of materials

GARAGES

DESIGN #PB5-14528
Price Code P8

1-CAR GARAGE

14'-0"

28'-0"

8' Ceiling

9'x7' Door

- Size - 14' x 28'
- Building height - 13'-0"
- Roof pitch - 6/12
- Ceiling height - 8'-0"

- 9' x 7' overhead door
- Handy side door allow for easy access
- Complete list of materials

2-CAR GARAGE WITH STORAGE

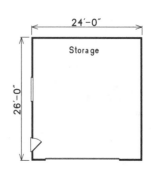

24'-0"

Storage

26'-0"

- Size - 24' x 26'
- Building height - 12'-8"
- Roof pitch - 4/12
- Ceiling height - 8'-0"
- 16' x 7' overhead door

- Plenty of storage space for yard equipment
- Convenient side door
- Complete list of materials
- Step-by-step instructions

2-CAR CARPORT WITH STORAGE

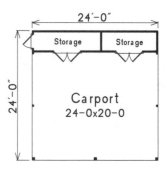

24'-0"

Storage   Storage

24'-0"

Carport
24-0x20-0

- Size - 24' x 24'
- Building height - 12'-8"
- Roof pitch - 4/12
- Ceiling height - 8'-0"

- Unique design allows cars to enter from the front or the side of carport
- Deep storage space for long or tall items
- Complete list of materials
- Step-by-step instructions

2-CAR GARAGE - HIP ROOF

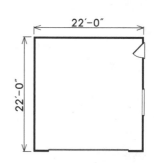

- Size - 22' x 22'
- Building height - 12'-2"
- Roof pitch - 4/12
- Ceiling height - 8'-0"
- 16' x 7' overhead door

- Handsome styling, ideal with many home types
- Practical side door
- Complete list of materials
- Step-by-step instructions

GARAGES

2-CAR GARAGE

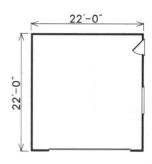

- Size - 22' x 22'
- Building height - 12'-2"
- Roof pitch - 4/12
- Ceiling height - 8'-0"
- 16' x 7' overhead door

- Useful side-entry door
- Perfect for tractor or lawn equipment
- Complete list of materials
- Step-by-step instructions

2-CAR GARAGE WITH WORKSHOP

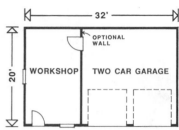

- Size - 32' x 20'
- Building height - 13'-0"
- Ceiling height - 8'-0"
- Roof pitch - 5/12

- Workshop ideal for storage, gardening or woodworking hobbies
- Outdoor entrance provides quick access
- Complete list of materials

1-CAR GARAGE

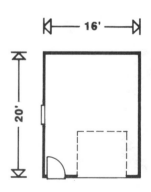

- Size - 16' x 20'
- Building height - 13'-0"
- Ceiling height - 8'-0"

- Roof pitch - 5/12
- Complete list of materials

2-CAR GARAGE - WESTERN STYLE/REVERSE GABLE

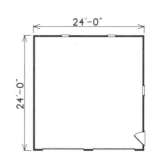

- Size - 24' x 24'
- Building height - 16'-7"
- Roof pitch - 8/12
- Ceiling height - 8'-0"

- Two 9' x 7' overhead doors
- Easy, functional design
- Complete list of materials
- Step-by-step instructions

DESIGN #PB5-14038
Price Code P6

2-CAR GARAGE - REVERSE GABLE

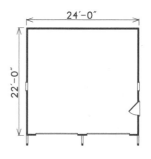

- Size - 24' x 22'
- Building height - 13'-0"
- Roof pitch - 5/12
- Ceiling height - 8'-0"
- Two 9' x 7' overhead doors

- Roof overhangs garage door to protect from the weather
- Handy side door
- Complete list of materials
- Step-by-step instructions

GARAGES

2-CAR GARAGE WITH STORAGE - REVERSE GABLE

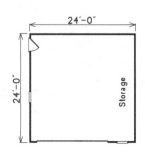

- Size - 24' x 24'
- Building height - 12'-8"
- Roof pitch - 4/12
- Ceiling height - 8'-0"
- 16' x 7' overhead door

- Windows on two sides
- Extra space perfect for storage
- Complete list of materials
- Step-by-step instructions

2-CAR GARAGE WITH STORAGE - HIP ROOF

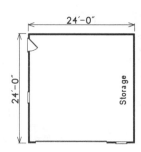

- Size - 24' x 24'
- Building height - 12'-6"
- Roof pitch - 4/12
- Ceiling height - 8'-0"

- 16' x 7' overhead door
- Side-entry provides easy access
- Complete list of materials
- Step-by-step instructions

DESIGN #PB5-14019
Price Code P7

2-CAR GARAGE - VICTORIAN

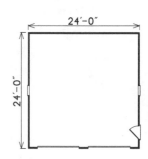

- Size - 24' x 24'
- Building height - 16'-7"
- Roof pitch - 8/12
- Ceiling height - 8'-0"
- Two 9' x 7' overhead doors

- Accented with Victorian details
- Functional side entry
- Complete list of materials
- Step-by-step instructions

GARAGES

DESIGN #PB5-14022
Price Code P6

2-CAR GARAGE

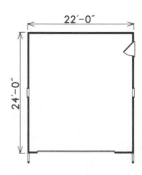

- Size - 22' x 24'
- Building height - 12'-2"
- Roof pitch - 4/12
- Ceiling height - 8'-0"
- 16' x 7' overhead door

- Attractive style for any home type
- Appealing side entry
- Complete list of materials
- Step-by-step instructions

1 1/2-CAR GARAGE WITH CARPORT

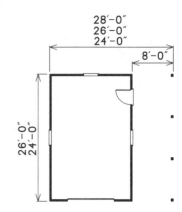

- Size -
  - 24' x 24'
  - 26' x 24'
  - 26' x 26'
  - 28' x 24'
- Building height - 13'-0"
- Roof pitch - 4/12

- Ceiling height - 8'-0"
- 9' x 7' overhead door
- Distinct hip roof design with spacious carport
- Complete list of materials
- Step-by-step instructions

2-CAR GARAGE WITH STORAGE

- Size - 25' x 26'
- Building height - 21'-0"
- Roof pitch - 10/12
- Ceiling height - 8'-0"

- Two 9' x 7' overhead doors
- Attractive styling with double gabled front facade and decorative window
- Complete list of materials

1-CAR GARAGE

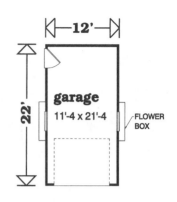

garage
11'-4 x 21'-4

FLOWER BOX

12'

22'

- Size - 12' x 22'
- Building height - 11'-6"
- Roof pitch - 5/12

- Charming flower boxes adorn both windows
- Complete list of materials
- Plans are printed on 8 1/2" x 11" pages

2-CAR GARAGE WITH STORAGE

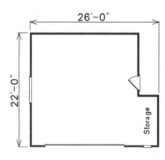

26'-0"

22'-0"

Storage

- Size - 26' x 22'
- Building height - 14'-10"
- Roof pitch - 7/12
- Ceiling height - 8'-0"
- 16' x 7' overhead door

- Attractive salt box style
- Includes additional storage
- Complete list of materials
- Step-by-step instructions

2-CAR GARAGE WITH GREENHOUSE

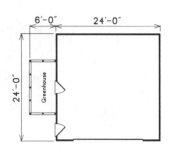

- Size - 30' x 24'
- Building height - 12'-8"
- Roof pitch - 4/12
- Ceiling height - 8'-0"
- 16' x 7' overhead door

- Unique design allows year-round gardening
- Additional space perfect for storing lawn equipment
- Complete list of materials
- Step-by-step instructions

2-CAR GARAGE WITH SUN DECK

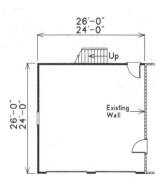

- Size -
  24' x 24'
  24' x 26'
  26' x 26'
- Building height - 12'-6"
- Ceiling height - 8'-0"

- Two 9' x 7' overhead doors
- Attached two-car garage with walk-out sun deck
- Complete list of materials
- Step-by-step instructions

2-CAR GARAGE -
ATTACHED OR DETACHED

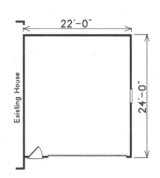

22'-0"

24'-0"

Existing House

- Size - 22' x 24'
- Building height - 12'-8"
- Roof pitch - 4/12
- Ceiling height - 8'-0"
- 16' x 7' overhead door

- Convenient service front door
- Traditionally styled
- Complete list of materials
- Step-by-step instructions

GARAGES

2-CAR GARAGE -
ATTACHED OR DETACHED

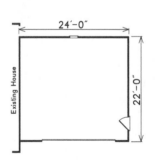

24'-0"

22'-0"

Existing House

- Size - 24' x 22'
- Building height - 14'-0"
- Roof pitch - 6/12
- Ceiling height - 8'-0"
- 16' x 7' overhead door

- Practical styling
- Wonderful versatility with this design
- Complete list of materials
- Step-by-step instructions

2-CAR GARAGE WITH LOFT

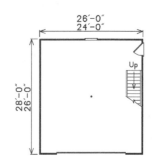

- **Size -**
  24' x 26'
  26' x 26'
  26' x 28'
- Building height - 23'-0"
- Roof pitch - 10/12 or 12/12

- Ceiling height - 8'-0"
- 16' x 7' overhead door
- Two-car eave entry garage has loft for additional storage
- Complete list of materials
- Step-by-step instructions

— DESIGN #PB5-14505 —
Price Code P8

2-CAR GARAGE WITH LOFT

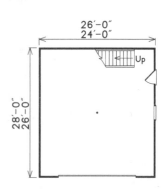

- **Size -**
  24' x 26'
  26' x 26'
  26' x 28'
- Building height - 23'-0"
- Roof pitch - 10/12 or 12/12

- Ceiling height - 8'-0"
- 16' x 7' overhead door
- Two-car garage has loft for additional storage
- Complete list of materials
- Step-by-step instructions

DESIGN #PB5-14501
Price Code P8

2-CAR GARAGE WITH LOFT

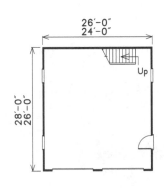

- Size -
  24' x 26'
  24' x 28'
  26' x 26'
  26' x 28'

- Building height - 23'-0"

- Roof pitch - 12/12

- Ceiling height - 8'-0"

- Two 9' x 7' overhead doors

- Tudor-style with studio/storage loft

- Complete list of materials

- Step-by-step instructions

DESIGN #PB5-14532
Price Code P8

2-CAR GARAGE

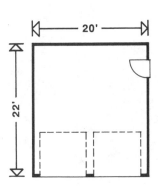

- Size - 20' x 22'

- Building height - 24'-6"

- Ceiling height - 8'-0"

- Roof pitch - 5/12

- Two 9' x 7' overhead doors

- Side entry door for easy access

- Complete list of materials

DESIGN #PB5-14533
Price Code P10

2-CAR GARAGE WITH STORAGE

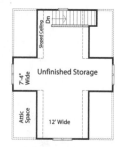

Second Floor

First Floor

- Size - 28' x 30'
- Building height - 25'-0"
- Ceiling heights -
  First Floor - 9'-0"
  Second Floor - 8'-0"

- Roof pitch - 12/12
- Attractive cupola and gables are appealing features to this garage
- Complete list of materials

DESIGN #PB5-14534
Price Code P10

2-CAR GARAGE WITH STORAGE

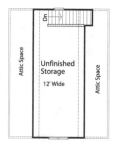

Second Floor

First Floor

- Size - 24' x 30'
- Building height - 25'-0"
- Ceiling heights -
  First Floor - 9'-0"
  Second Floor - 8'-0"

- Roof pitch - 12/12
- Attractive cupola adds country charm to the exterior
- Complete list of materials

2-CAR GARAGE WITH 8' HIGH DOOR

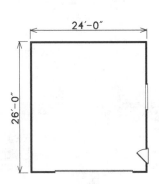

24'-0"

26'-0"

- Size - 24' x 26'
- Building height - 13'-8"
- Roof pitch - 4/12
- Ceiling height - 9'-0"
- 16' x 8' overhead door

- Practical and appealing
- Side window adds light
- Complete list of materials
- Step-by-step instructions

2-CAR GARAGE WITH STORAGE

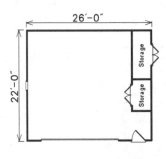

26'-0"

22'-0"

Storage

Storage

- Size - 26' x 22'
- Building height - 13'-0"
- Roof pitch - 4/12
- Ceiling height - 8'-0"
- 16' x 7' overhead door

- Provides two separate lockable storage compartments with and one accessible from the outside
- Helpful addition to your home
- Complete list of materials
- Step-by-step instructions

GARAGES

DESIGN #PB5-14048
Price Code P7

3-CAR GARAGE

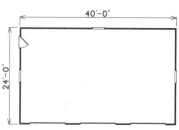

40'-0"

24'-0"

- Size - 40' x 24'
- Building height - 15'-6"
- Roof pitch - 6/12
- Ceiling height - 9'-0"
- Three 9' x 7' overhead doors

- Oversized with plenty of room for storage
- Side door for easy access
- Complete list of materials
- Step-by-step instructions

DESIGN #PB5-14535
Price Code P10

2-CAR AND R.V. GARAGE WITH LOFT

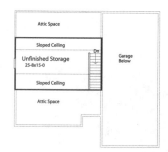

Attic Space

Sloped Ceiling

Unfinished Storage
25-8x15-0

Dn

Garage
Below

Sloped Ceiling

Attic Space

Second Floor

44'-0"

Garage
25-6x33-0

9' Ceiling

RV Garage
17-0x39-0

16' Ceiling

Up

40'-0"

16'x8' Door

12'x14' Door

First Floor

- Size - 44' x 40'
- Building height - 25'-0"
- Ceiling heights -
  First Floor - 9'-0"
  Second Floor - 8'-0"

- Roof pitch - 9/12, 10/12
- Unfinished storage could easily be converted to an office or workshop
- Complete list of materials

DESIGN #PB5-14016
Price Code P8

2-CAR GARAGE WITH LOFT

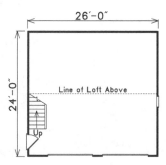

26'-0"

24'-0"

Line of Loft Above

Up

- Size - 26' x 24'
- Building height - 20'-0"
- Roof pitch - 6/12
- Ceiling height - 8'-0"
- Two 9' x 7' overhead doors

- Loft provides extra storage area or workshop space
- Clerestory windows brighten inside
- Complete list of materials
- Step-by-step instructions

GARAGES

DESIGN #PB5-14025
Price Code P7

2 1/2-CAR GARAGE - WESTERN STYLE

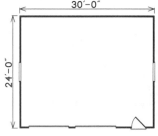

30'-0"

24'-0"

- Size - 30' x 24'
- Building height - 12'-6"
- Roof pitch - 4/12
- Ceiling height - 8'-0"
- Two 9' x 7' overhead doors

- Plenty of storage space
- Additional space perfect for workshop
- Complete list of materials
- Step-by-step instructions

2-CAR GARAGE WITH WORKSHOP AND PARTIAL LOFT

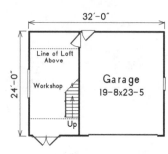

- Size - 32' x 24'
- Building height - 20'-2"
- Roof pitch - 10/12
- Ceiling height - 9'-8"
- Workshop and loft ceiling height - 8'-0"

- 16' x 7' overhead door, 6'-0" x 6'-8" double-door
- Convenient loft above workshop for work space or storage
- Complete list of materials
- Step-by-step instructions

2 1/2-CAR GARAGE

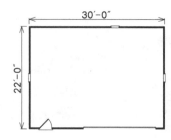

- Size - 30' x 22'
- Building height - 12'-2"
- Roof pitch - 4/12
- Ceiling height - 8'-0"
- 16' x 7' overhead door

- Additional space perfect for yard equipment storage
- Door allows easy access to and from storage space
- Complete list of materials
- Step-by-step instructions

2-CAR GARAGE WITH DORMERS

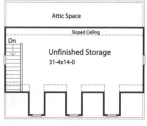

Second Floor

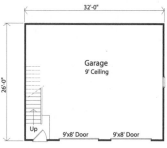

First Floor

- Size - 32' x 26'
- Building height - 26'-0"
- Ceiling heights -
  First Floor - 9'-0"
  Second Floor - 8'-0"

- Roof pitch - 12/12
- Trio of dormers fills unfinished storage with plenty of natural light
- Complete list of materials

2-CAR GARAGE WITH RV/BOAT STORAGE

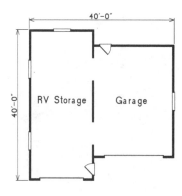

- Size - 40' x 40'
- Building height - 21'-0"
- Roof pitch - 6/12
- Ceiling height - 16'-0" RV Storage

- Ceiling height - 10'-0" Garage
- 12' x 14' and 16' x 8' overhead doors
- Excellent garage for large equipment, R.V. or boat storage
- Complete list of materials

4-CAR GARAGE WITH WORKSHOP

- Size - 62' x 34'
- Building height - 17'-0"
- Roof pitch - 6/12, 8/12
- Ceiling height - 9'-0"

- Three 16' x 8' overhead doors
- Spacious workshop area includes a convenient half bath
- Complete list of materials

3-CAR GARAGE WITH STORAGE

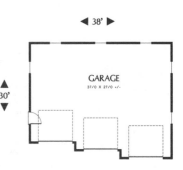

- Size - 38' x 30'
- Building height - 22'-0"
- Roof pitch - 10/12
- Ceiling height - 9'-0"

- Three 9' x 8' overhead doors
- Attractive styling fits well with most every home
- Complete list of materials

2-CAR GARAGE

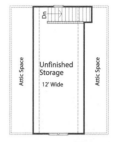

Second Floor

First Floor

- Size - 24'-0" x 30'-4"
- Building height - 25'-0"
- Ceiling heights -
  First Floor - 9'-0"
  Second Floor - 8'-0"

- Roof pitch - 12/12
- Unfinished storage area could easily be converted to a secluded office area
- Complete list of materials

GARAGES

2-CAR AND RV GARAGE WITH LOFT

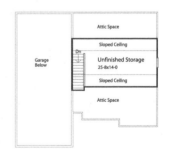

Second Floor

First Floor

- Size - 44' x 40'
- Building height - 25'-0"
- Ceiling heights -
  First Floor - 9'-0", 16'-0"
  Second Floor - 8'-0"

- Roof pitch - 9/12, 10/12
- Unfinished storage is ideal for extra camping equipment
- Complete list of materials

3-CAR GARAGE WITH LOFT - WESTERN STYLE

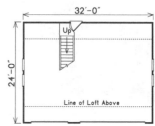

- Size - 32' x 24'
- Building height - 20'-6"
- Roof pitch - 12/12
- Ceiling height - 8'-0"

- 16' x 7', 9' x 7' overhead doors
- Large side windows draw in light
- Complete list of materials
- Step-by-step instructions

2-CAR GARAGE WITH WORKSHOP/STORAGE

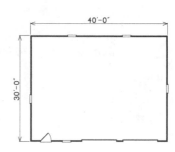

- Size - 40' x 30'
- Building height - 16'-7"
- Roof pitch - 5/12
- Ceiling height - 10'-0"

- Two 10' x 9' overhead doors
- Oversized garage is ideal as a workshop or boat storage
- Complete list of materials

DESIGN #PB5-14012
Price Code P7

3-CAR GARAGE

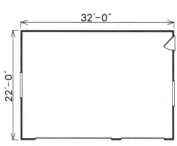

- Size - 32' x 22'
- Building height - 12'-2"
- Roof pitch - 4/12
- Ceiling height - 8'-0"
- 9' x 7' and 16' x 7' overhead doors

- Side-entry for easy access
- Perfect style with many types of homes
- Complete list of materials
- Step-by-step instructions

GARAGES

DESIGN #PB5-14026
Price Code P7

3-CAR GARAGE

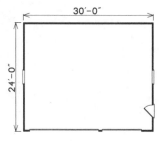

- Size - 30' x 24'
- Building height - 13'-8"
- Roof pitch - 5/12
- Ceiling height - 8'-0"
- 16' x 7', 9' x 7' overhead doors

- Highly functional design
- Handy side-entry door
- Complete list of materials
- Step-by-step instructions

HORSE BARN - 2 STALL

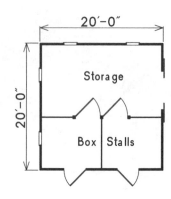

20'-0"

20'-0"

Storage

Box Stalls

- Size - 20' x 20'
- Partial slab foundation at storage
- Building height - 12'-8"
- Roof pitch - 5/12

- Ceiling height - 8'-0"
- Compact, yet extra storage for feed
- 6' x 7' sliding side door into storage area
- Complete list of materials

HORSE BARN - 4 STALL

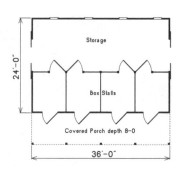

Storage

24'-0"

Box Stalls

Covered Porch depth 8-0

36'-0"

- Size - 36' x 32'
- Slab foundation
- Building height - 13'-4"
- Roof pitch - 4/12
- Ceiling height - 8'-0"

- Four box stalls with doors to covered walkway
- Includes tack area, feed storage and 8' x 7' sliding doors
- Complete list of materials

POLE BUILDING - HORSE BARN

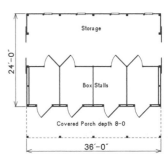

- Size - 36' x 32'
- Building height - 14'-9"
- Roof pitch - 4/12
- Wall height - 9'-0"
- Spacious feed storage area

- Two 8' x 8' sliding doors and four 4' x 7' Dutch doors
- Walkway connects all four stalls and leads to tack area
- Complete list of materials
- Step-by-step instructions

HORSE BARN WITH LOFT

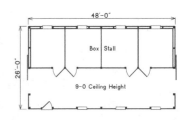

- Size - 26' x 48'
- Building height - 22'-0"
- Roof pitch - 6/12, 12/6
- Loft ceiling height - 11'-0"
- Features four box stalls

- Two 8' x 8' sliding doors and one 5' x 7' sliding door at loft
- Loft designed for 75 p.s.f. live load
- Complete list of materials
- Step-by-step instructions

BUILDINGS

POLE BUILDING/SHOP/GARAGE

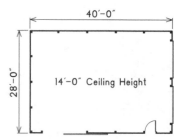

40'-0"

28'-0"

14'-0" Ceiling Height

- Size - 40' x 28'
- Building height - 19'-6"
- Roof pitch - 4/12
- Two 10' x 10' overhead doors
- One 12' x 12' sliding door
- Designed for easy maintenance
- Complete list of materials
- Step-by-step instructions

DESIGN #PB5-15016
Price Code P8

POLE BUILDING - OPEN SHED

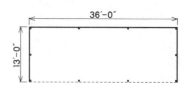

36'-0"

13'-0"

- Size - 36' x 13'
- 8' or 10' front wall height
- Lofting storage or machinery storage
- Building can be lengthened by adding additional 12' bays
- Complete list of materials
- Step-by-step instructions

POLE BUILDING - EQUIPMENT SHED

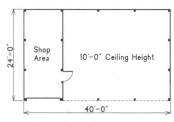

- Size - 40' x 24'
- Building height - 14'-4"
- Roof pitch - 4/12
- This design can be lengthened by adding as many 10' bays as needed

- 9' x 8' overhead door
- Separated space with door perfect for workshop or storage
- Complete list of materials
- Step-by-step instructions

BUILDINGS

DESIGN #PB5-15007
Price Code P8

POLE BUILDING

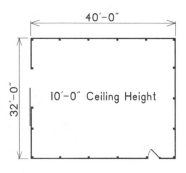

- Size - 32' x 40'
- Building height - 16'-0"
- Roof pitch - 4/12

- 10' x 8' sliding door
- Complete list of materials
- Step-by-step instructions

SCREENED PORCH

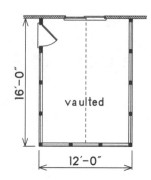

16'-0"

vaulted

12'-0"

- Size - 12' x 16'
- Pier foundation
- Building height - 12'-6"
- Roof pitch - 6/12
- Wall height - 8'-0"

- Vaulted ceiling creates spaciousness
- Adds value to your home
- Complete list of materials
- Step-by-step instructions

SUNROOM ADDITION

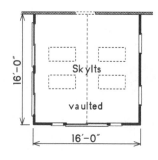

16'-0"

Skylts

vaulted

16'-0"

- 256 square feet
- Crawl space foundation
- Building height - 13'-6"
- Roof pitch - 6/12
- Wall height - 8'-0"

- Skylights brighten interior
- Sliding glass doors bring the outdoors in
- Space could also be a private home office
- Complete list of materials
- Step-by-step instructions

SCREENED PORCH

- Size - 16'-6" x 12'-3"
- Building height - 13'-0"
- Roof pitch - 6/12
- Wall height - 8'-0"
- Perfect addition to any home
- Features vaulted ceiling for spaciousness
- Complete list of materials
- Step-by-step instructions

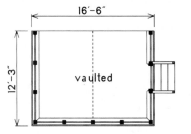

BUILDINGS

3 SEASONS ROOM

- 325 square feet
- Building height - 13'-6"
- Roof pitch - 6/12
- Wall height - 8'-0"
- Perfect for entertaining
- Plenty of sunlight permits plants and flowers
- Complete list of materials
- Step-by-step instructions

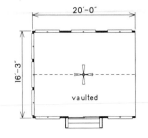

STUDIO HOME OFFICE

- 432 square feet
- Crawl space or slab foundation, please specify when ordering
- Building height - 19'-6"
- Roof pitch - 12/12
- Ceiling height - 9'-0"
- 2" x 6" exterior walls
- Studio/home office is flooded with sunlight from large windows
- French door accesses covered porch
- Complete list of materials

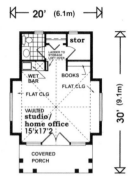

WORKROOM WITH COVERED PORCH

- Size - 24' x 20'
- Slab foundation
- Building height - 13'-6"
- Roof pitch - 6/12
- Ceiling height - 8'-0"
- Double-door entry
- Interior enhanced by large windows
- Complete list of materials
- Step-by-step instructions

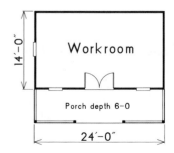

DESIGN #PB5-15502
Price Code P13

WOODED GETAWAY

- 676 square feet
- Crawl space foundation
- Building height - 17'-9"
- Roof pitch - 6/12
- Ceiling height - 8'-0"
- 1 bedroom, 1 bath
- Open design has fireplace and full-length porch
- Complete list of materials

DESIGN #PB5-15511
Price Code P6

WEEKENDER COTTAGE

- 144 square feet
- Building height -14'-6"
- Ceiling height - 10'-0"
- 2" x 6" exterior walls
- Slab foundation
- Roof pitch - 12/12 and 5/12
- Could easily be an office or guest house
- Multiple built-ins make storage simple
- Complete list of materials

COUNTRY CABIN

- 416 square feet
- Slab foundation
- Building height - 14'-0"
- Roof pitch - 6/12
- Ceiling height - 8'-0"
- Sleeping area, 1 bath
- Economical design for a small lot is a perfect retreat
- Complete list of materials

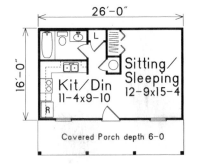

26'-0"

16'-0"

Kit/Din
11-4x9-10

Sitting/
Sleeping
12-9x15-4

Covered Porch depth 6-0

2-CAR GARAGE APARTMENT

- 588 square feet
- Building height - 23'-0"
- Roof pitch - 12/12 and 4/12
- Ceiling heights -
  First floor - 8'-0"
  Second floor - 8'-0"
- Charing dormers add character to exterior
- 1 bedroom, 1 bath
- Complete list of materials

First Floor   Second Floor

28'(8.5 m)

24'(7.3 m)

UP

k/din
14'6x8'

br
11'x10'

liv
12'6x11'

DN

2-CAR GARAGE APARTMENT WITH DORMERS

- 652 square feet
- Building height - 23'-0"
- Ceiling height - 8'-0"
- Roof pitch - 3 1/2/12, 11/12
- 1 bedroom, 1 bath
- Complete list of materials

Second Floor

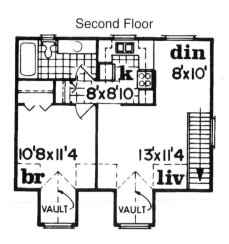

din 8'x10'

k 8'x8'10

10'8"x11'4

br

VAULT

13'x11'4

liv

VAULT

Width: 28'-0"
Depth: 26'-0"

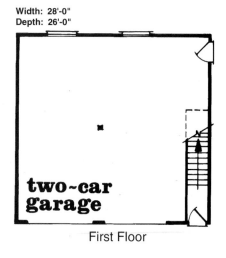

two-car garage

First Floor

BUILDINGS

COZY COTTAGE

- 576 square feet
- Crawl space foundation
- Building height - 16'-0"
- Roof pitch - 6/12
- Ceiling height - 8'-0"
- 1 bedroom, 1 bath
- Perfect country retreat features vaulted living room with skylights and plant shelf above
- Complete list of materials

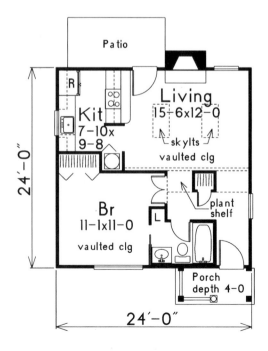

STONE COTTAGE

- 647 square feet
- Crawl space foundation
- Building height - 17'-0"
- Roof pitch - 10/12
- Wall height - 8'-0"
- 1 living/sleeping room, 1 bath
- Large vaulted room for living/ sleeping with plant shelves on each end, stone fireplace and sunken bath
- Complete list of materials

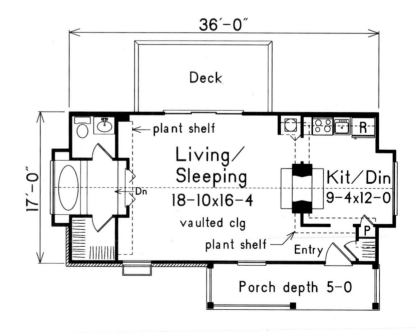

POLE BUILDINGS

- Four popular sizes -

  24' x 32'   24' x 40'

  32' x 40'   32' x 48'

- Building height - 15'-6" with 10' ceiling height
- Building height - 17'-6" with 12' ceiling height
- Two 5' x 10' or two 6' x 12' sliding doors
- Designed for easy maintenance
- Complete list of materials
- Step-by-step instructions

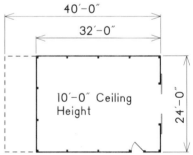

10'-0" Ceiling Height

40'-0"

32'-0"

24'-0"

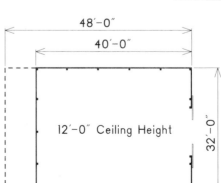

12'-0" Ceiling Height

48'-0"

40'-0"

32'-0"

3-CAR GARAGE APARTMENT

- 974 square feet
- Building height - 23'-2"
- Roof pitch - 5/12
- Ceiling height - 8'-0"
- 2 bedrooms, 1 bath
- Three 9' x 7' overhead doors
- Efficiently designed kitchen and breakfast room combine with living area for spaciousness
- Complete list of materials

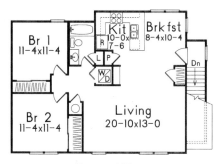

Second Floor

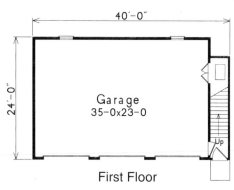

First Floor

MULTI-PURPOSE BARN

- Size - 24' x 36'
- Building height - 23'-8"
- Roof pitch - 4/12, 12/4
- Two 9' x 9' sliding doors
- Loft ceiling height - 9'-9"
- 5'x6' loft double-door
- Ideal machine storage or as a three-stall horse barn
- Loft designed for 100 p.s.f. live load
- Complete list of materials
- Step-by-step instructions

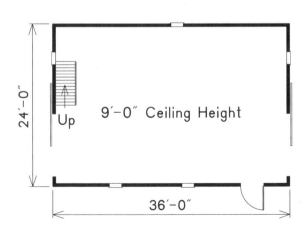

24'-0"

Up

9'-0" Ceiling Height

36'-0"

2-CAR GARAGE APARTMENT

- 840 square feet
- Building height - 25'-8"
- Roof pitch - 7/12
- Ceiling heights -
  First Floor - 9'-0"
  Second Floor - 8'-0"
- 1 bedroom, 1 bath
- Two 9' x 7' overhead doors
- Cozy covered entry
- Complete list of materials

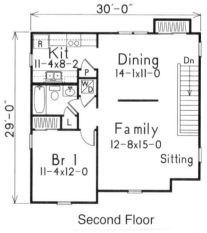

Second Floor

First Floor

3-CAR GARAGE APARTMENT

- 676 square feet
- Building height - 22'-0"
- Roof pitch - 12/12
- Ceiling height - 8'-0"
- 1 bedroom, 1 bath
- Complete list of materials

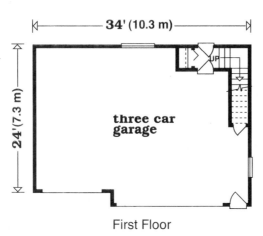

Second Floor

WIC
k 11'2x8'
F
L
br 10'x12'
W D
HWT
liv 12'4x15'
DN

34' (10.3 m)

24' (7.3 m)

UP

three car garage

First Floor

2-CAR GARAGE APARTMENT WITH STONE ACCENTS

- 1,671 square feet
- Building height - 29'-0"
- Roof pitch - 8/12, 10/12, 5.5/12
- Ceiling height - 8'-0"
- 16' x 7' overhead door
- 3 bedrooms, 2 1/2 baths, 2-car garage
- Two-story entry with hallway leads to family room, dining area and U-shaped kitchen
- Basement foundation
- Complete list of materials

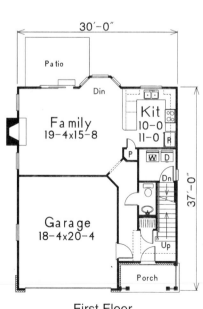

First Floor

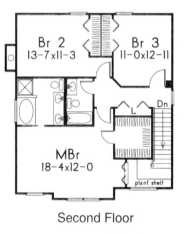

Second Floor

BUILDINGS

3-CAR APARTMENT GARAGE
WITH COUNTRY FLAIR

- 929 square feet
- Building height - 27'-0"
- Roof pitch - 6.5/12, 10/12
- Ceiling heights -
  First floor - 9'-0"
  Second floor - 8'-0"
- 16' x 8', 9' x 8' overhead doors
- 2 bedrooms, 1 bath, 3-car side entry garage
- Slab foundation
- Spacious living room with dining area has access to 8' x 12' deck through glass sliding doors
- Complete list of materials

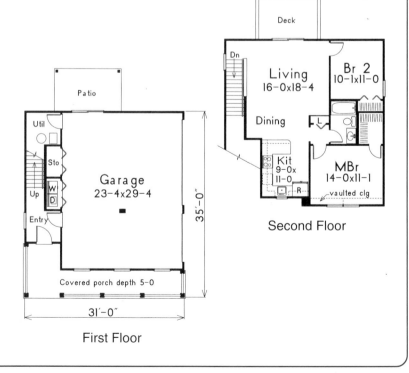

First Floor

Second Floor

2-CAR GARAGE APARTMENT

- 654 square feet
- Building height - 24'-0"
- Roof pitch - 7/12
- Ceiling height - 8'-0"
- 16' x 7' overhead door
- 1 bedroom, 1 bath
- Vaulted living room is open to a pass-through kitchen and breakfast bar with an overhead plant shelf and sliding glass doors to an outside balcony
- Complete list of materials

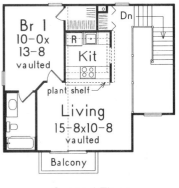

Second Floor

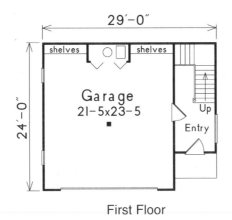

First Floor

BUILDINGS

2-CAR GARAGE APARTMENT

- 628 square feet
- Building height - 26'-6"
- Roof pitch - 8/12, 9/12
- Ceiling heights -
  First floor 9'-0"
  Second floor 8'-0"
- 16' x 7' overhead door
- 1 bedroom, 1 bath
- Cozy living room offers vaulted ceiling, fireplace and a pass-through kitchen
- Complete list of materials

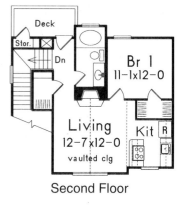

Second Floor

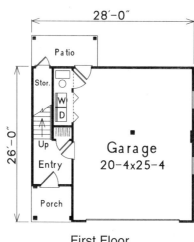

First Floor

POLE BUILDING - MACHINE SHED

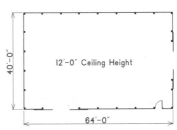

12'-0" Ceiling Height

40'-0"

64'-0"

- Size - 40' x 64'
- Building height - 20'-0"
- Roof pitch - 4/12
- Two 8' x 10' sliding doors on two sides of building

- Complete list of materials
- Step-by-step instructions

BUILDINGS

LARGE POOLSIDE STRUCTURE

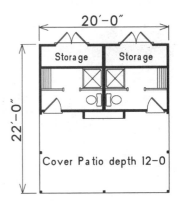

20'-0"

Storage   Storage

22'-0"

Cover Patio depth 12-0

- Size - 20' x 22'
- Slab foundation
- Building height - 13'-5"
- Roof pitch - 6/12
- Ceiling height - 8'-0"

- Two dressing areas both with shower and toilet
- Covered area ideal for snack/drink bar
- Storage area accessible to outdoors for lawn and pool equipment
- Complete list of materials
- Step-by-step instructions

CABIN WITH WRAP-AROUND PORCH

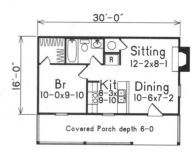

- 720 square feet
- Crawl space foundation, drawings also include slab foundation
- Building height - 14'-0"
- Roof pitch - 4/12
- Ceiling height - 8'-0"
- 2 bedrooms, 1 bath
- Large covered porch provides plenty of outdoor living space
- Complete list of materials

DESIGN #PB5-15506
Price Code P11

EXCLUSIVE RETREAT

- 480 square feet
- Slab foundation
- Building height - 14'-2"
- Roof pitch - 6/12
- Ceiling height - 8'-0"
- 1 bedroom, 1 bath
- Cozy cabin includes large fireplace in sitting area with views into dining area
- Complete list of materials

ROOM ADDITION

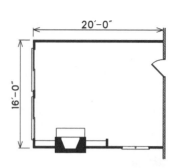

- 320 square feet
- Crawl space foundation
- Building height - 13'-6"
- Roof pitch - 6/12
- Ceiling height - 8'-0"

- Appealing addition to your home
- Two sets of sliding glass doors make it accessible to the outdoors
- Makes a perfect family room, sunroom or bedroom
- Complete list of materials
- Step-by-step instructions

BUILDINGS

DESIGN #PB5-15501
Price Code P13

TRADITIONAL COTTAGE

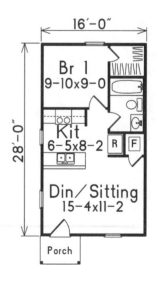

- 448 square feet
- Slab foundation
- Building height - 14'-0"
- Roof pitch - 8/12
- Ceiling height - 8'-0"

- 1 bedroom, 1 bath
- Compact design is perfect for weekend getaways
- Complete list of materials

DESIGN #PB5-15014
Price Code P10

A-FRAME COTTAGE

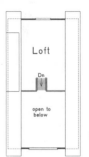

Loft
240 sq. ft.

First Floor
720 sq. ft.

- 960 square feet
- Pier foundation
- Building height - 22'-0"
- Roof pitch - 24/12
- 1 bedroom, 1 sleeping loft and 1 bath

- Open central living area is functional and spacious
- Plenty of storage throughout
- Complete list of materials
- Step-by-step instructions

DESIGN #PB5-15017
Price Code P10

3-CAR CARPORT WITH APARTMENT

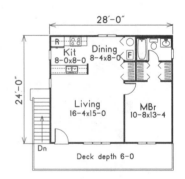

- 672 square feet
- Building height - 22'-0" with 8'-0" carport height
- Roof pitch - 4/12
- Apartment can double as vacation getaway

- 1 bedroom, 1 bath
- Complete list of materials
- Step-by-step instructions

SPORT CABIN

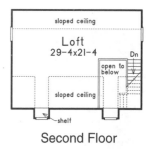

- 576 square feet
- Pier foundation
- Building height - 25'-6"
- Roof pitch - 6/12
- Ceiling height - 8'-0"

- 2 bedrooms, 1 bath
- Ideal for avid hunter or fisherman
- Complete list of materials
- Step-by-step instructions

WORKSHOP WITH LOFT

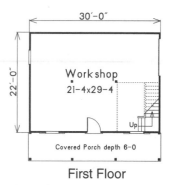

Second Floor

First Floor

- Size - 30' x 22'
- Slab foundation
- Building height - 20'-6"
- Roof pitch - 8/12, 6/12
- Ceiling height - 8'-0"

- 8' x 7' overhead door
- Open floor plan has ample work space and additional storage with loft above
- Complete list of materials

BUILDINGS

2-CAR GARAGE APARTMENT - TUDOR STYLE

Second Floor

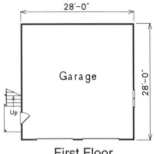

First Floor

- 784 square feet
- Building height - 24'-6"
- Roof pitch - 6/12
- Ceiling height - 8'-0"
- Two 9' x 7' overhead doors

- 1 bedroom, 1 bath
- Outdoor covered stairs shelter from the elements
- Complete list of materials
- Step-by-step instructions

2-CAR GARAGE APARTMENT - WESTERN STYLE

Second Floor

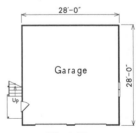

First Floor

- 784 square feet
- Building height - 24'-6"
- Roof pitch - 6/12
- Ceiling height - 8'-0"
- Two 9' x 7' overhead doors

- 1 bedroom, 1 bath
- Open living area is functional
- Space for utilities off the kitchen
- Complete list of materials
- Step-by-step instructions

CRAFT COTTAGE

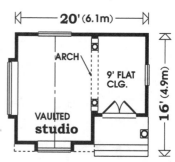

- 288 square feet
- Building height - 16'-8"
- Ceiling height - 9'-0"
- 2" x 6" exterior walls
- Crawl space foundation, drawings also include slab foundation

- Roof pitch - 12/12, 5/12
- Vaulted studio makes ideal artist's retreat or craft workshop
- Double French doors access covered porch
- Complete list of materials

BUILDINGS

2-CAR GARAGE APARTMENT WITH INTERIOR ENTRANCE

Second Floor

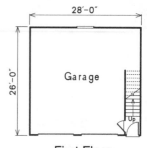

First Floor

- 746 square feet
- Building height - 22'-0"
- Roof pitch - 4/12
- Ceiling height - 8'-0"

- Two 9' x 7' overhead doors
- 1 bedroom, 1 bath
- Complete list of materials
- Step-by-step instructions

DESIGN #PB5-15517
Price Code P11

2-CAR GARAGE APARTMENT

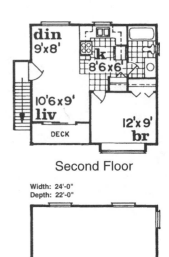

Second Floor

Width: 24'-0"
Depth: 22'-0"

two~car garage

First Floor

- 484 square feet
- Building height - 25'-0"
- Ceiling height - 8'-0"

- Roof pitch - 7/12
- 1 bedroom, 1 bath
- Complete list of materials

DESIGN #PB5-15508
Price Code P12

3-CAR GARAGE APARTMENT WITH STORAGE

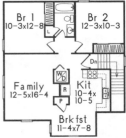

Second Floor

First Floor

- 973 square feet
- Building height - 24'-8"
- Roof pitch - 6/12
- Ceiling height - 8'-0"
- 2 bedrooms, 1 bath

- 16' x 7' and 9' x 7' overhead doors
- Sunny breakfast room positioned between the kitchen and the living area for convenience
- Complete list of materials

DESIGN #PB5-15518
Price Code P12

2-CAR GARAGE APARTMENT

Second Floor

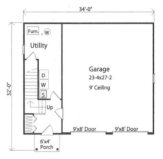

First Floor

- 1,240 square feet
- Building height - 27'-0"
- Roof pitch - 9/12, 12/12, 6/12
- Ceiling heights -
  First Floor - 9'-0"
  Second Floor - 8'-0"

- 2 bedrooms, 1 bath
- Kitchen/breakfast combine for added spaciousness
- Sloped ceiling adds appeal in sitting area
- Complete list of materials

DESIGN #PB5-15027
Price Code P9

2-CAR GARAGE APARTMENT - STUDIO

Second Floor

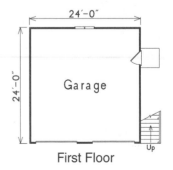

First Floor

- 576 square feet
- Building height - 21'-6"
- Roof pitch - 4/12
- Ceiling height - 8'-0"
- Two 9' x 7' overhead doors

- Contemporary style with private outdoor entrance
- Complete list of materials
- Step-by-step instructions

2-CAR GARAGE APARTMENT - CAPE COD

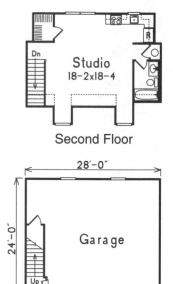

Second Floor

First Floor

- 566 square feet
- Building height - 22'-0"
- Roof pitch - 12/12, 4.5/12
- Ceiling heights-
  First Floor - 8'-0"
  Second Floor - 7'-7"

- Two 9' x 7' overhead doors
- Charming dormers add appeal to this design
- Comfortable open living area
- Complete list of materials
- Step-by-step instructions

3-CAR GARAGE WITH BONUS ROOM

Second Floor

First Floor

- 686 square feet on second floor
- Building height - 25'-6"
- Roof pitch - 10/12
- Ceiling heights -
  First floor - 12'-0"
  Second floor - 8'-0"

- Three 9' x 10' overhead doors
- Vaulted bonus room would make an ideal home office or hobby area
- Complete list of materials

3-CAR GARAGE APARTMENT

Second Floor

First Floor

- 1,032 square feet
- Building height - 24'-0"
- Roof pitch - 5/12, 10/12
- Ceiling heights - 8'-0"
- 2 bedrooms, 1 bath

- Spacious family room flows into kitchen/breakfast area
- Two sunny bedrooms share a bath
- Complete list of materials

2-CAR GARAGE APARTMENT - GAMBREL ROOF

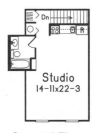

Second Floor

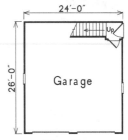

First Floor

- 438 square feet
- Building height - 21'-3"
- Roof pitch - 6/12, 12/6
- Ceiling heights-
  First Floor - 8'-0"
  Second Floor - 7'-9"

- Two 9' x 7' overhead doors
- Comfortable colonial-styling
- Simple yet spacious studio design
- Complete list of materials
- Step-by-step instructions

DESIGN #PB5-15026
Price Code P10

2-CAR GARAGE APARTMENT - GAMBREL ROOF

Second Floor

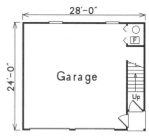

First Floor

- 604 square feet
- Building height - 21'-4"
- Roof pitch - 4/12, 12/4.75
- Ceiling height - 8'-0"
- Two 9' x 7' overhead doors

- Charming Dutch colonial style
- Spacious studio provides extra storage space
- Complete list of materials
- Step-by-step instructions

DESIGN #PB5-15030
Price Code P9

2-CAR GARAGE APARTMENT WITH EXTERIOR ENTRANCE

Second Floor

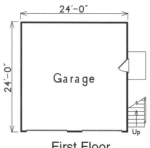

First Floor

- 576 square feet
- Building height - 21'-5"
- Roof pitch - 4/12
- Ceiling height - 8'-0"
- Two 9' x 7' overhead doors

- Loft has roomy kitchen and dining area
- Private side exterior entrance
- Style complements many types of homes
- Complete list of materials
- Step-by-step instructions

2-CAR GARAGE APARTMENT

BR.
12/0 X 10/0

DN

W/D

LIVING
16/6 X 12/4

SHELVES

Second Floor

◀ 28' ▶

GARAGE
23/0 X 25/0

UP

▲ 26' ▼

First Floor

- 633 square feet
- Building height - 24'-0"
- Roof pitch - 9/12
- Ceiling height - 8'-0"
- 1 bedroom, 1 bath

- Two 8' x 7' overhead doors
- Lots of storage throughout including built-in shelves and a desk in the living area
- Complete list of materials

BUILDINGS

2-CAR GARAGE APARTMENT

Attic Space

Dn

P R L

Sitting
10-9x14-0

Kit.

Sleeping
9-2x8-8

Second Floor

34'-0"

Garage
9' Ceiling

26'-0"

Up

9'x8' Door   9'x8' Door

7'x4' Covered Porch

First Floor

- 568 square feet
- Building height - 26'-0"
- Roof pitch - 12/12
- Ceiling heights -
  First Floor - 9'-0"
  Second Floor - 8'-0"

- 1 bedroom/sleeping area, 1 bath
- Beautiful dormers brighten interior
- Complete list of materials

3-CAR GARAGE APARTMENT

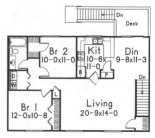

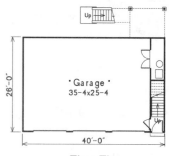

Second Floor

First Floor

- 1,040 square feet
- Building height - 23'-0"
- Roof pitch - 5/12
- Ceiling height - 8'-0"
- Three 9' x 7' overhead doors

- 2 bedrooms, 1 bath
- Large rooms offer comfortable living with second floor laundry, ample cabinets and sliding doors to deck
- Complete list of materials

2-CAR GARAGE APARTMENT

Second Floor

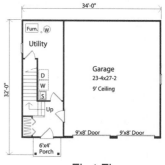

First Floor

- 1,240 square feet
- Building height - 27'-0"
- Roof pitch - 9/12, 12/12, 6/12
- Ceiling heights -
  First Floor - 9'-0"
  Second Floor - 8'-0"

- Kitchen/breakfast area includes island ideal for food preparation or dining
- Spacious bath directly accesses the bedroom as well as the sitting area
- Complete list of materials

DESIGN #PB5-15032
Price Code P12

3-CAR GARAGE APARTMENT - CAPE COD

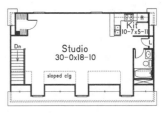

Second Floor

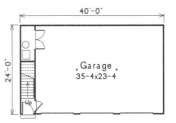

First Floor

- 813 square feet
- Building height - 22'-0"
- Roof pitch - 12/12, 4.25/12
- Ceiling height - 8'-0"
- Three 9' x 7' overhead doors

- Studio, 1 bath
- Spacious studio apartment with kitchen and bath
- Perfect for recreation, in-law or home office
- Complete list of materials

BUILDINGS

DESIGN #PB5-15505
Price Code P12

3-CAR GARAGE APARTMENT

Second Floor

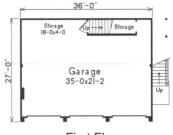

First Floor

- 949 square feet
- Building height - 24'-10"
- Roof pitch - 6/12
- Ceiling heights -
  First Floor - 9'-0"
  Second Floor - 8'-0"

- 1 bedroom, 1 bath
- Three 9' x 7' overhead doors
- Sitting area includes an attractive window seat which becomes focal point
- Complete list of materials

2-CAR APARTMENT GARAGE W/ATRIUM

Second Floor

First Floor

- 902 square feet
- Building height - 27'-4"
- Roof pitch - 9/12
- Ceiling height -
  First Floor - 9'-0"
  Second Floor - 8'-0"

- Two 9'x8' overhead doors
- 1 bedroom, 1 bath
- Large living room connects to an L-shaped kitchen with pantry and dining area/balcony
- Complete list of materials

2-CAR GARAGE APARTMENT

- 665 square feet
- Slab foundation
- Building height - 17'-0"
- Roof pitch - 6/12, 8/12
- Ceiling height - 8'-0"

- 1 bedroom, 1 bath
- Spacious breakfast/sitting area flow into kitchen area
- Complete list of materials

EIGHT-SIDED GAZEBO

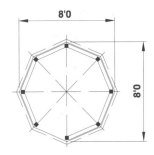

- Size - 8' x 8'
- Building height - 13'-0"
- Graceful accents make this gazebo one-of-a-kind
- Complete list of materials
- Plans come printed on 8 1/2" x 11" pages

ARBOR/BENCH

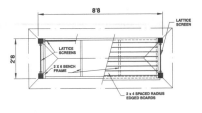

- Size - 8'-8" x 2'-8"
- Building height - 10'-4"
- Attractive enclosing lattice screens
- Roof provides shelter from the elements
- Complete list of materials
- Plans are printed on 8 1/2" x 11" pages

DECKS & GAZEBOS

HIGH-LOW DECK

- Upper deck size - 10'-0" x 8'-0"
  Lower deck size - 15'-6" x 13'-0"
- Designed as an add-on to an existing deck or as a complete unit
- Benches can be arranged as needed
- Features a unique conversation area or optional in-ground fireplace
- Complete list of materials
- Step-by-step instructions

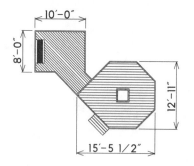

TIERED DECK WITH GAZEBO

- Sizes -
  Overall area - 28'-6" x 15'-6" (without gazebo)
  Deck "A" - 9'-0" x 15'-6"
  Deck "B" - 6'-6" x 8'-6"
  Deck "C" - 14'-0" x 12'-0"
  Gazebo "D" - 9'-6"x8'-3" sided
  Walkway "E" - 3'-0" x 7'-0"
- Build complete or add on later
- Complete list of materials
- Step-by-step instructions

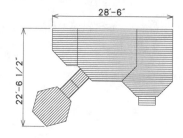

ENTRY PORCHES

- Size - 8'-0" x 5'-9"
- Two popular styles - contemporary and colonial
- Attractive designs to fit any type of home
- Can be free-standing or attached
- Adaptable for trailer or home use
- Complete list of materials
- Step-by-step instructions

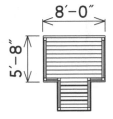

PATIO COVERS - ROOF/SUN SHADE

PATIO ROOF

SUN SHADE

- Patio roof size - 16' x 9'
- Sun shade size - 20' x 10'
- A unique and functional addition to your home
- Complete list of materials
- Step-by-step instructions

DECKS & GAZEBOS

TWO LEVEL GARDEN DECK

- Overall size - 16' x 19'

  Main deck - 16' x 12'

  Upper deck - 8' x 8'

- Design has decorative plant display area or sundeck
- Built-in seating
- Can be free standing or attached
- Complete list of materials
- Step-by-step instructions

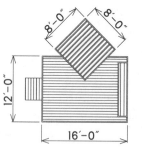

DECK ENHANCEMENTS

- Four unique designs -

  planter box - 2'-0" x 2'-0"

  decorative screen - 7'-0" x 5'-6"

  bench - 6'-0" x 1'-8"

  end table - 2'-6" x 1'-5"

- Adds to any existing deck
- Can be free standing or attached to your deck
- Complete list of materials
- Step-by-step instructions

DESIGN #PB5-13003
Price Code P4

EXPANDABLE DECKS

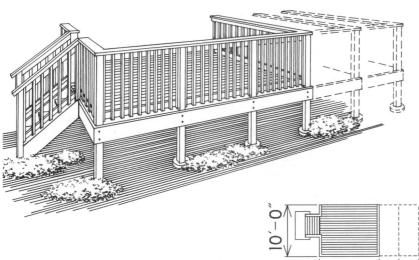

- Six popular sizes -
12' x 10'	12' x 12'
16' x 10'	16' x 12'
20' x 10'	20' x 12'

- Functional decks in a variety of sizes to fit your every need

- Complete list of materials

- Step-by-step instructions

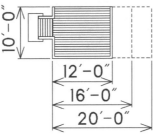
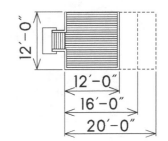

DESIGN #PB5-13030
Price Code P3

ENTRY PORCHES

PLAN 1

PLAN 2

- Two popular styles -

  Plan 1 - 6'-5" x 5'-5"

  Plan 2 - 7'-5" x 6'-5"

- Functional porches that enhance any entrance

- Complete list of materials

- Step-by-step instructions

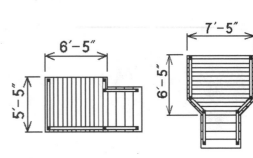

SHADED DECK

- Size - 16'-0" x 10'-0" x 9'-6" high
- Deck design has a sun screen covering
- Enhance your outdoors with this shaded deck
- Complete list of materials
- Step-by-step instructions

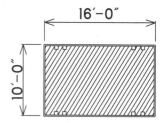

16'-0"

10'-0"

PATIO COVERS

- Two sizes -
  12' x 13'
  16' x 13'
- Designed to cover an existing deck or patio or used as a pavilion
- Can be built with standard lumber
- Plan includes an alternate bench design
- Complete list of materials
- Step-by-step instructions

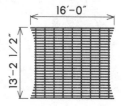

16'-0"

13'-2 1/2"

GARDEN ENTRYWAY

- Size - 8' x 8'
- Height peak to grade - 10'-10"
- Unique, attractive design that will complement either your garden or home
- Simple construction
- Complete list of materials
- Step-by-step instructions

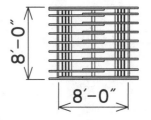

8'-0"

8'-0"

FOUR-SIDED GAZEBO

- Size - 10' x 8'
- Height from top of floor to peak - 11'-0"
- Gable roof construction
- A unique and functional addition to your yard
- Adds additional shade and privacy for outdoor entertaining
- Complete list of materials
- Step-by-step instructions

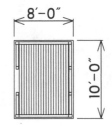

8'-0"

10'-0"

DECKS & GAZEBOS

OCTAGON-SHAPED SUN DECK

- Size -
  9' diameter
  12' diameter
  16' diameter

- Easy-to-build deck makes a great hot tub platform or freestanding sun deck

- Complete list of materials

- Step-by-step instructions

ANGULAR LOW-LEVEL DECK

- Size -
  20' x 14'
  24' x 18'
  28' x 22'

- Angular design is ideal for a home with elegant lines on a flat lot

- Complete list of materials

- Step-by-step instructions

CASUAL CURVED DECK

- Size -
  16' x 8'
  16' x 10'
  16' x 12'
  20' x 12'

- Planter and bench details included

- Complete list of materials

- Step-by-step instructions

CONTEMPORARY CURVED DECK

- Size -
  24' x 14'
  26' x 14'
  28' x 14'

- Curved design adapts to any home

- Bench details included

- Complete list of materials

- Step-by-step instructions

DECKS & GAZEBOS

GARDEN GAZEBO

- Size -
  10' x 10'
  12' x 12'
  16' x 16'
- A picturesque backyard getaway
- Complete list of materials
- Step-by-step instructions

NOSTALGIC GAZEBO

- Size -
  9' diameter
  12' diameter
  16' diameter
- Elegant design adapts to multi-seasonal use
- Complete list of materials
- Step-by-step instructions

TWO-LEVEL DECK

- Overall size - 14' x 15'

  lower deck - 8' x 8'

  upper deck - 12' x 9'

- Unique, attractive design features a two-level deck and bench

- Adds great value to your home

- Complete list of materials

- Step-by-step instructions

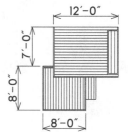

TWO-LEVEL SPA DECK

- Overall size - 20'-0" x 14'-0"

  upper deck - 10'-9" x 11'-3"

  lower deck - 14'-9" x 14'-0"

- Designed for self-contained portable spas

- Free standing or next to house

- Complete list of materials

- Step-by-step instructions

DECKS & GAZEBOS

EIGHT-SIDED VICTORIAN GAZEBO

- Size - 12' x 12'
- Building height - 17'-0"
- Victorian accents create a charming feel
- Elegant weathervane enhances the structure
- Provides wonderful place for outdoor entertaining
- Complete list of materials
- Plans are printed on 8 1/2" x 11" pages

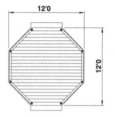

DESIGN #PB5-13514
Price Code P6

TEN-SIDED GAZEBO

- Size - 11'-5" x 12'-0"
- Building height - 16'-0"
- Unique gazebo that is easy to build
- Complete list of materials
- Plans are printed on 8 1/2" x 11" pages

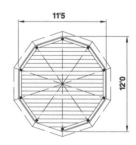

POOL DECK

- Size - 16' x 14'
- Can be built to fit any size pool
- Simple but sturdy design with built-in gate
- Helps cleaning and maintaining the pool a breeze
- Complete list of materials
- Step-by-step instructions

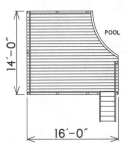

DESIGN #PB5-13012
Price Code P3

EASY DECKS

- Three great sizes -
  8' x 12'
  12' x 12'
  16' x 12'
- Low cost construction
- Can be built with standard lumber
- Adaptable to all grades
- Complete list of materials
- Step-by-step instructions

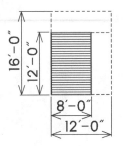

DECKS & GAZEBOS

MID-LEVEL DECK

- Size -
  14' x 10'
  16' x 12'
  20' x 12'
- Charming deck fits any home style
- Bench and planter details included
- Complete list of materials
- Step-by-step instructions

SPLIT-LEVEL DECK

- Size -
  12' x 14'
  16' x 14'
  20' x 14'
- Cantilevered deck can be easily adapted for any height
- Complete list of materials
- Step-by-step instructions

CUSTOM SPLIT-LEVEL DECK

- Upper Deck size - 12' x 8'

  Lower Deck size - 22' x 16'
  24' x 16'
  26' x 16'

- Spacious deck can accommodate the needs of today's active lifestyle
- Complete list of materials
- Step-by-step instructions

MULTI-LEVEL DECK WITH SPA

- Upper deck size - 18' x 10'

  Lower deck size - 27' x 20'-6"

- Perfectly designed getaway for backyard relaxation and recreation
- Complete list of materials
- Step-by-step instructions

DECKS & GAZEBOS

SPLIT-LEVEL DECK

- Overall size - 20' x 14'

  upper deck - 12' x 12'

  lower deck - 9' x 8'

- Can be built with standard lumber

- Adaptable to all grades

- Complete list of materials

- Step-by-step instructions

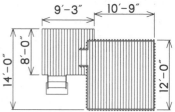

TWO-LEVEL RAISED DECK

- Overall size - 21'-0" x 24'-0"

  upper deck - 12'-0" x 12'-9"

  lower deck - 18'-0" x 12'-0"

- Can be built at any height

- Adaptable to any lot situation

- Complete list of materials

- Step-by-step instructions

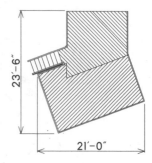

LOW PATIO DECKS

- Three popular sizes -
  12' x 12'
  16' x 12'
  20' x 12'
- Built-in seating
- Perfect for entertaining
- Complete list of materials
- Step-by-step instructions

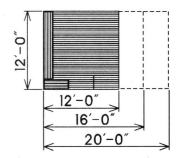

BAY DECK WITH RAILING

DECKS & GAZEBOS

- Size - 20'-6" x 12'-6"
- Adds beauty and value to your home
- Unique layout with built-in bay
- Complete list of materials
- Step-by-step instructions

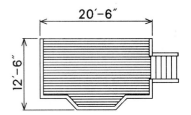

DECK WITH GAZEBO

- Size - 24'-0" x 15'-6"
- Height floor to peak - 12'-2"
- Perfect for outdoor entertaining
- Gazebo adds unique flair to this deck
- Complete list of materials
- Step-by-step instructions

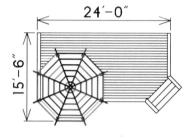

SIX-SIDED GAZEBO

- Size - 8'-3" x 9'-6"
- Height floor to peak - 12'-10"
- Complements any setting
- Cozy gazebo great for entertaining a small group
- Complete list of materials
- Step-by-step instructions

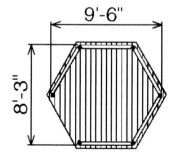

RAISED PATIO DECKS

- Two popular sizes -
  12' x 12'
  16' x 12'

- Both decks can be con-
  structed at any height

- Can be built to fit any lot
  situation

- Complete list of materials

- Step-by-step instructions

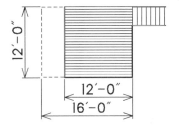

DECK WITH SUNKEN DINING AREA

- Two popular sizes -
  18' x 18'
  20' x 20'

- Unique sunken area adds
  interest to this deck

- Perfect addition to en-
  hance outdoor entertaining

- Complete list of materials

- Step-by-step instructions

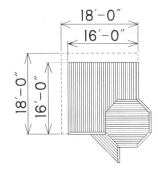

DECKS & GAZEBOS

3 BRIDGES

PLAN 1

PLAN 2

PLAN 3

- Three styles and sizes -
  Plan 1 - 18'-0" x 5'-0"
  Plan 2 - 13'-5" x 5'-0"
  Plan 3 - 11'-0" x 5'-0"
- Enhance your outdoors
- Complete list of materials
- Step-by-step instructions

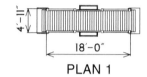

4'-11"

18'-0"

PLAN 1

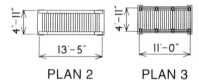

4'-11"

13'-5"

PLAN 2

4'-11"

11'-0"

PLAN 3

SQUARE GAZEBO

- Size - 12' x 12'
- Building height - 16'-6"
- Roof pitch 12/12
- Complete list of materials
- Plans are printed on
  8 1/2" x 11" pages

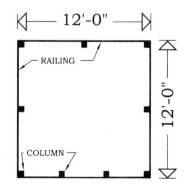

12'-0"

12'-0"

RAILING

COLUMN

OCTAGON GAZEBO

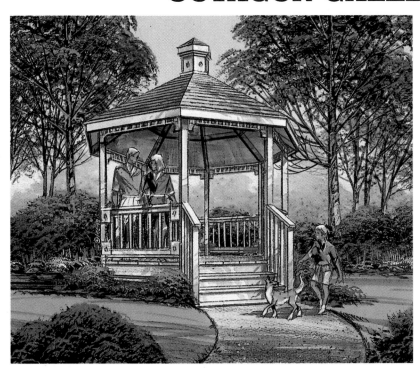

- Size - 11'-6" x 11'-6"
- Height floor to peak - 14'-7"
- Large gazebo has plenty of space for outdoor entertaining
- This attractive structure will complement any setting
- Complete list of materials
- Step-by-step instructions

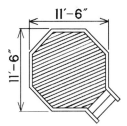

EASY PATIO COVER

- Size - 16' x 12'
- Attractive patio cover features a sun screen covering
- Adds value and beauty to your home
- Complete list of materials
- Step-by-step instructions

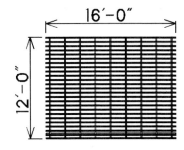

DECKS & GAZEBOS

Jungle #PB5-WA75014

Make your child's room a very special place.

It's easy as 1 - 2 - 3.

Create the wonderful look you want for your baby's nursery with a mural you can paint yourself — no artistic ability required! Our Paint-by-Number Wall Mural kits include everything you need even the paint. We make it so easy, you can do it in a weekend!

Over 90 Designs for Nursery & Children's Rooms
Order online at www.wallartdesigns.com.

To request a catalog by phone, call toll-free,
877-WALL MURAL (877-925-5687)

Murals are available in 3 sizes, priced from $49.97 - $99.97

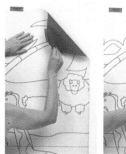

TAPE

TRACE

PAINT

Treehouse Mural #PB5-76304

Baby Carousel Mural #PB5-75015

Bench & Plants Mural #PB5-77104

Butterflies Mural #PB5-75701

Celestial Mural #PB5-75013

Dancin' Dinos Mural #PB5-75501

Flamingo Island Mural #PB5-76703

Home Run Mural #PB5-76907

Jungle Mural #PB5-75014

Pledge Allegiance Mural #PB5-75911

Rainbow Fantasy Mural #PB5-76101

Speedway Mural #PB5-76501

WALL ART

Note: Paint colors used on walls in photos may vary slightly from the paint colors provided in the kit.

Scroll Saw Patterns are simple and easy projects that include step-by-step instructions, a detailed material list and a color picture or photo as a guide. These do-it yourself patterns include toys, shelves and functional furniture.

PURCHASE ANY TWO ITEMS* ON PAGES 152-157 & RECEIVE THE THIRD ITEM FREE.
*excluding graphite paper - Item #PB5-YA30000

Item #PB5-39001
Curio w/Diamonds
36"x4¹/₂"x30"

Item #PB5-39002
Curio
15"x4¹/₂"x30"

Item #PB5-39003
24" Heart Shelf
24"x5¹/₂"x6¹/₄"

Item #PB5-39004
34" Heart Shelf
34"x5¹/₂"x6¹/₄"

Item #PB5-39005
18" Heart Shelf
18"x4¹/₂"x6¹/₂"

Item #PB5-39006
Baseball Wall Plaque
13"x4¹/₄"x10¹/₂"

Item #PB5-39007
3 Sport Wall Plaque
8¹/₂"x30"x11"

Item #PB5-39008
Remote Holder
8"x8³/₄"x6³/₄"

Item #PB5-39009
34" Towel Bar w/Shelf
34"x7"x12"

Item #PB5-39010
Towel Bar w/ Shelf
25¹/₂"x7"x12"

Item #PB5-39011
Heart Quilt Rack
25¹/₂"x9¹/₄"x32"

Item #PB5-39012
Quilt Rack
25¹/₂"x9¹/₄"x32"

Item #PB5-39013
2 Shelf Plant Stand
31¹/₂"x9¹/₄"x33"

Item #PB5-39014
3 Shelf Bookcase
36"x9¹/₄"x40"

Item #PB5-39015
Heart Table
14"x11³/₄"x23¹/₂"

Item #PB5-39016
Rocking Horse
30"x11"x23³/₄"

Item #PB5-39017
Recipe Box
13"x9¹/₂"x4¹/₂"

Item #PB5-39018
Phone Stand
14"x9"x32"

Item #PB5-39019
Book Shelf
31¹/₂"x11¹/₄"x33"

Item #PB5-39020
Cactus Magazine Rack
21¹/₂"x11¹/₄"x20¹/₄"

Item #PB5-39021
Star Magazine Rack
17¹/₂"x9³/₄"x13¹/₂"

Item #PB5-39022
Cup Holder
8¹/₄"x8¹/₄"x19¹/₄"

Item #PB5-39023
Hat & Coat Rack
34"x4¹/₄"x4³/₄"

Item #PB5-39024
Heart Magazine Rack
16¹/₂"x7"x15"

Item #PB5-39025
Southwestern Towel Bar
33¹/₂"x6¹/₄"x8"

Item #PB5-39026
Corner Shelf w/ Cactus
17"x8¹/₂"x6"

Item #PB5-39027
Duxbury Shelf
32"x6¹/₂"x10³/₄"

SCROLL SAW PATTERNS
All Patterns Price Code P2

Item #PB5-39028
Plymouth Shelf
24"x6³/₄"x10³/₄"

Item #PB5-39029
Corner Heart Shelf
7¹/₂"x7¹/₂"x11"

Item #PB5-39030
Corner Shelf
7¹/₂"x7¹/₂"x24³/₄"

Item #PB5-39031
Heart Shaped Stool
13³/₄"x10¹/₄"x6¹/₄"

Item #PB5-39032
Potato Box
12³/₄"x11¹/₄"x37¹/₂"

Item #PB5-39033
Bread Box
19³/₄"x11¹/₄"x11"

Item #PB5-39034
Key/Mail Holder
11"x3"x9"

Item #PB5-39035
Large Shadow Box
21"x4"x25¹/₂"

Item #PB5-39036
Curio Shelf w/Cactus & Pegs
16¹/₂"x2¹/₂"x13¹/₂"

Item #PB5-39037
Star Shelf w/Pegs
12"x3³/₄"x19¹/₂"

Item #PB5-39038
Barn Bird House
11¹/₄"x7¹/₂"x12³/₄"

Item #PB5-39039
Blue Bird House
9"x7"x11¹/₄"

Item #PB5-39040
Heart Bird House
13¹/₂"x11"x8"

Item #PB5-39041
Traditional Bird House
10¹/₂"x10"x11¹/₄"

Item #PB5-39042
Trad. Magazine Rack
17"x9¹/₄"x14¹/₂"

Item #PB5-39043
Cactus Shelf
24"x7¹/₂"x15¹/₂"

Item #PB5-39044
Victorian Bird House
13¹/₂"x11¹/₄"x17³/₄"

Item #PB5-39045
Bird Feeder
11¹/₄"x11¹/₄"x10³/₄"

Item #PB5-39046
Pyramid Wine Rack
21¹/₄"x9¹/₂"x17¹/₂"

Item #PB5-39047
Heart Shadow Box
22¹/₂"x2³/₄"x17¹/₂"

Item #PB5-39048
Southwest Corner Shelf
7¹/₂"x7¹/₂"x12³/₄"

Item #PB5-39049
Children's Bug Keeper
8"x2¹/₄"x6¹/₂"

Item #PB5-39050
H. Dryer/C. Iron Holder
7¹/₄"x4³/₄"x14"

Item #PB5-39051
Kitchen Rack
12³/₄"x3¹/₄"x15³/₄"

Item #PB5-39052
Coffee Pot Shelf & Rack
22"x3¹/₂"x15¹/₄"

Item #PB5-39053
Key Rack with Doors
9"x3"x13¹/₂"

Item #PB5-39054
Cactus Coat Rack
19¹/₂"x5¹/₂"x11¹/₄"

Item #PB5-39055
Telephone Rack
17¹/₂"x11¹/₄"x30"

Item #PB5-39056
Blanket/Quilt Rack
26¹/₂"x14¹/₄"x30"

Item #PB5-39057
Traditional End Table
25"x17¹/₄"x20"

SCROLL SAW

Yard Art full-size trace-on patterns are simple and easy, do-it-yourself patterns that include easy to follow instructions, a list of tools and supplies needed and a color picture or photo as a guide. These do-it yourself patterns include holiday, non-seasonal and lawn and garden. Some patterns create a scene and some stand alone.

To enable easy transfer of the Yard Art patterns to your material, we offer jumbo graphite transfer paper (ITEM #PB5-30000). Each sheet is 18" x 36" and is non-smear, erasable and reusable. These patterns are fun for people of all ages and provide hours of fun and creativity. All Yard Art Patterns are Price Code P2 and are $10.00 each.

Item #PB5-30000
Graphite Paper
18" x 36"

Product
Sample

Item #PB5-30002
2 Candy Canes
22" x 26"

Item #PB5-30003
Penguin/Box
32" x 41"

Item #PB5-30004
Penguins with Sign
35" x 45"

Item #PB5-30005
Penguins with Sled
48" x 28"

Item #PB5-30006
Mary, Joseph & Jesus
43" x 35"

Item #PB5-30007
Wisemen
29" x 60"

Item #PB5-30008
Camel/Donkey
58" x 35"

Item #PB5-30009
Shepherd/Sheep
50" x 35"

Item #PB5-30010
Sheep
35" x 54"

Item #PB5-30011
Donkey
24" x 48"

Item #PB5-30012
Flying Deer/Legs In
21" x 34"

Item #PB5-30013
Flying Deer/Legs Out
45" x 35"

Item #PB5-30014
Santa/Flying Sleigh
41" x 38"

YARD ART
All Patterns Price Code P2

Item #PB5-30015
Santa Engineer
46" x 35"

Item #PB5-30016
Ho Ho Express
41" x 35"

Item #PB5-30017
Elf In Train
39" x 34"

Item #PB5-30018
Caboose
41" x 33"

Item #PB5-30019
Santa Stop Here
35" x 46"

Item #PB5-30020
Falling Santa with
Reindeer
52" x 35"

Item #PB5-30021
Climbing Reindeer
24" x 70"

Item #PB5-30022
Reindeer/Elf Dancing
41" x 46"

Item #PB5-30023
Elf on Reindeer
43" x 41"

Item #PB5-30024
Elves with Presents
48" x 35"

Item #PB5-30025
Holiday Greetings
35" x 47"

Item #PB5-30026
Kids with Star
41" x 44"

Item #PB5-30027
Kids Music Parade
68" x 35"

Item #PB5-30028
Caroler Kids
41" x 42"

Item #PB5-30030
Nutcracker
43" x 41"

Item #PB5-30031
Mr. Chip Snowman
24" x 48"

Item #PB5-30032
Mrs. Chip Snowman
24" x 46"

Item #PB5-30033
Mr. Snowman
30" x 48"

Item #PB5-30034
Mrs. Snowman
29" x 48"

Item #PB5-30035
Texas Snowman
35" x 68"

Item #PB5-30036
M/M Spotted Dog
35" x 41"

Item #PB5-30037
Puppies/Wreath
34" x 42"

Item #PB5-30038
Puppies/Red Bulb
25" x 41"

Item #PB5-30039
Singing Mice
34" x 54"

Item #PB5-30040
Mrs. Claus Waving
28" x 47"

Item #PB5-30041
Mr. Claus Waving
28" x 47"

Item #PB5-30042
Frosty
27" x 46"

Item #PB5-30043
Christmas Tree
47" x 69"

Item #PB5-30044
Skating Snowman
30" x 45"

Item #PB5-30045
Skating Snowlady
33" x 45"

YARD ART

Item #PB5-30046
Nativity
47" x 35"

Item #PB5-30047
Nativity Animals
29" x 22"

Item #PB5-30048
Santa In Chimney
36" x 32"

Item #PB5-30049
Santa's Workshop
42" x 36"

Item #PB5-30050
North Pole Greeting
36" x 40"

Item #PB5-30051
Igloo
45" x 36"

Item #PB5-30052
Angel with Star
23" x 43"

Item #PB5-30053
Flying Angel with Star
39" x 26"

Item #PB5-30054
Peppermint
23" x 28"

Item #PB5-30055
Old World Santa
59" x 23"

Item #PB5-30056
Saint Nicklaus
35" x 53"

Item #PB5-30057
Keep Warm
39" x 35"

Item #PB5-30058
Santa Stop Moose
35" x 49"

Item #PB5-30059
Mr. Kringle
35" x 39"

Item #PB5-30060
Mrs. Kringle
27" x 38"

Item #PB5-30061
Santa Noel
21" x 53"

Item #PB5-30062
Snowman in Sleigh
30" x 35"

Item #PB5-30063
Country Reindeer
35" x 41"

Item #PB5-30064
Welcome Winter
39" x 35"

Item #PB5-30065
Country Snowman
44" x 35"

Item #PB5-30066
Let it Snow
35" x 41"

Item #PB5-30067
Mr. Woodsy Snowman
35" x 33"

Item #PB5-30068
Mrs. Woodsy Snowman
31" x 33"

Item #PB5-30069
Father Christmas
29" x 59"

Item #PB5-31001
Ghost In Pumpkin
21" x 31"

Item #PB5-31002
Cat on Pumpkin
35" x 31"

Item #PB5-31003
Frankenstein
25" x 61"

Item #PB5-31004
Haunted House
34" x 69"

Item #PB5-31005
Mummy
23" x 47"

Item #PB5-31006
Boo Ghost
31" x 36"

YARD ART
All Patterns Price Code P2

Item #PB5-31007
Scarecrow/Fence
53" x 35"

Item #PB5-31008
Pumpkin Patch
40" x 33"

Item #PB5-31009
Witch w/Pot
31" x 50"

Item #PB5-31011
Skeleton w/Tombstone
40" x 43"

Item #PB5-31012
Trick or Treat Fence
36" x 62"

Item #PB5-31013
Witch on Broom
48" x 33"

Item #PB5-31014
Bat Atop Pumpkin
36" x 33"

Item #PB5-31015
Fall Scene
39" x 35"

Item #PB5-31016
Kitten on Fence
32" x 48"

Item #PB5-31017
Scarecrow
35" x 47"

Item #PB5-31018
Vampire at Tombstone
40" x 35"

Item #PB5-31019
Flying Boo Ghost
38" x 35"

Item #PB5-31020
Witch/Ghost Broom
35" x 33"

Item #PB5-31021
Ghost & Witch
46" x 36"

Item #PB5-31022
Zombie
36" x 44"

Item #PB5-31023
Witch's Brew
36" x 36"

Item #PB5-31024
Pumpkin Parade
50" x 23"

Item #PB5-32001
It's a Girl/Boy
32" x 47"

Item #PB5-32002
Mr. Fannie
36" x 43"

Item #PB5-32003
Mrs Fannie
36" x 47"

Item #PB5-32004
Ducks/Chickens/Pigs
35" x 40"

Item #PB5-32005
Squirrels/Rabbits/Skunks
34" x 38"

Item #PB5-32006
Donkey with Basket
56" x 33"

Item #PB5-32007
Dog Biting Boy's Pants
44" x 35"

Item #PB5-32008
Silhouette Cowboy
19" x 58"

Item #PB5-32009
Silhouette Gentleman
21" x 59"

Item #PB5-32010
Cute Cow
40" x 35"

YARD ART

YARD ART/SCROLL SAW ORDER FORM

CALL TOLL-FREE **1-800-373-2646** (Day or Night)

Three Easy Ways To Order Plans
1. Call toll-free 1-800-373-2646 for credit card orders.
2. FAX your Order to 1-314-770-2226.
3. Mail the Order Form to the address below.

For Faster Service Order Plans By Phone
You may call us anytime and charge your order on MasterCard, Visa, American Express or Discover. Most orders are processed within 24 hours of receipt. For U.S. orders please allow 7 working days for delivery. If you need to place a rush order, please call us by 11:00 a.m. CST and ask for overnight or second day service.

Important Notice
The right of building only one structure from the plans purchased is licensed exclusively to the buyer and the plans may not be resold. **Note that plans are specifically printed for each order and are not returnable. Prices are subject to change without notice.**

QUESTIONS? Call Our Customer Service Number 314-770-2228

YARD ART.

I hereby authorize HDA, Inc. to charge this purchase to my credit card account (check one):

☐ MasterCard   ☐ VISA   ☐ DISCOVER NOVUS   ☐ AMERICAN EXPRESS Cards

My card number is _____

The expiration date is _____

Signature _____

Name _____
(Please print or type)

Street Address _____
(Please **do not** use P.O. Box)

City, State, Zip _____

My daytime phone number (_____) - _____ - _____

Mail to: HDA, Inc.
4390 Green Ash Drive
St. Louis, MO 63045-1219

Please send me Item No(s): _____ $ _____
_____ $ _____
_____ $ FREE!
_____ $ _____
_____ $ _____
_____ $ FREE!

_____ Graphite Paper @ $2.95 ea. $ _____
SUBTOTAL $ _____
SALES TAX (MO residents add 7%) $ _____
SHIPPING & HANDLING $ _____
TOTAL ENCLOSED (US funds only) $ _____

☐ Enclosed is my check or money order payable to HDA, Inc. (Sorry, no COD's) **Prices subject to change without notice.**

YARD ART.

I hereby authorize HDA, Inc. to charge this purchase to my credit card account (check one):

☐ MasterCard   ☐ VISA   ☐ DISCOVER NOVUS   ☐ AMERICAN EXPRESS Cards

My card number is _____

The expiration date is _____

Signature _____

Name _____
(Please print or type)

Street Address _____
(Please **do not** use P.O. Box)

City, State, Zip _____

My daytime phone number (_____) - _____ - _____

Mail to: HDA, Inc.
4390 Green Ash Drive
St. Louis, MO 63045-1219

Please send me Item No(s): _____ $ _____
_____ $ _____
_____ $ FREE!
_____ $ _____
_____ $ _____
_____ $ FREE!

_____ Graphite Paper @ $2.95 ea. $ _____
SUBTOTAL $ _____
SALES TAX (MO residents add 7%) $ _____
SHIPPING & HANDLING $ _____
TOTAL ENCLOSED (US funds only) $ _____

☐ Enclosed is my check or money order payable to HDA, Inc. (Sorry, no COD's) **Prices subject to change without notice.**

PROJECT PLANS INDEX

PROJECT PLAN ORDER FORM

IMPORTANT INFORMATION TO KNOW BEFORE YOUR ORDER

- **Exchange Policies** - Since blueprints are printed in response to your order, we cannot honor requests for refunds. However, if for some reason you find that the plan you have purchased does not meet your requirements, you may exchange that plan for another plan in our collection. At the time of the exchange, you will be charged a processing fee of 25% of your original plan package price, plus the difference in price between the plan packages (if applicable) and the cost to ship the new plans to you.

  Please note: Reproducible drawings can only be exchanged if the package is unopened, and exchanges are allowed only within 90 days of purchase.

- **Building Codes & Requirements** - At the time the construction drawings were prepared, every effort was made to ensure that these plans and specifications meet nationally recognized codes. Our plans conform to most national building codes. Because building codes vary from area to area, some drawing modifications and/or the assistance of a professional designer or architect may be necessary to comply with your local codes or to accommodate specific building site conditions. We advise you to consult with your local building official for information regarding codes governing your area.

BLUEPRINT PRICE SCHEDULE

Price Code	1-Set	Additional Sets	Reproducible Masters
P3	$15.00	$10.00	$65.00
P4	$20.00	$10.00	$70.00
P5	$25.00	$10.00	$75.00
P6	$30.00	$10.00	$80.00
P7	$50.00	$10.00	$100.00
P8	$75.00	$10.00	$125.00
P9	$125.00	$20.00	$200.00
P10	$150.00	$20.00	$225.00
P11	$175.00	$20.00	$250.00
P12	$200.00	$20.00	$275.00
P13	$225.00	$45.00	$440.00

Plan prices guaranteed through December 31, 2004.
Please note that plans are not refundable.

SHIPPING & HANDLING CHARGES

EACH ADDITIONAL SET ADD $2.00 TO SHIPPING CHARGES

U.S. SHIPPING

Regular *(allow 7-10 business days)* $5.95
Priority *(allow 3-5 business days)* $15.00
Express* *(allow 1-2 business days)* $25.00

CANADA SHIPPING

Standard *(allow 8-12 business days)* $15.00
Express* *(allow 3-5 business days)* $40.00

OVERSEAS SHIPPING/INTERNATIONAL

Call, fax, or e-mail (plans@hdainc.com) for shipping costs.
* For express delivery please call us by 11:00 a.m. CST

How To Order

For fastest service, Call Toll-Free
1-800-373-2646 day or night

Three Easy Ways To Order

1. CALL toll free 1-800-373-2646 for credit card orders. MasterCard, Visa, Discover and American Express are accepted.
2. FAX your order to 1-314-770-2226.
3. MAIL the Order Form to:

HDA, Inc.
4390 Green Ash Drive
St. Louis, MO 63045

QUESTIONS?
Call Our Customer Service Number
314-770-2228

ORDER FORM

Please send me -

PLAN NUMBER PB5- ____________

PRICE CODE ______ (see Plan Page)

Reproducible Masters (see chart at left) $ ______
Initial Set of Plans $ ______
Additional Plan Sets (see chart at left)
_____ (Qty) at $ ______ each $ ______

SUBTOTAL $ ______
SALES TAX (MO residents add 7%) $ ______
☐ Shipping / Handling (see chart at left) $ ______
(each additional set add $2.00 to shipping charges)

TOTAL ENCLOSED (US funds only) $ ______

☐ Enclosed is my check or money order payable to HDA, Inc. (Sorry, no COD's)

I hereby authorize HDA, Inc. to charge this purchase to my credit card account (check one):

☐ MasterCard ☐ VISA ☐ DISCOVER NOVUS ☐ AMERICAN EXPRESS Cards

Credit Card number ____________

Expiration date ____________

Signature ____________

Name ____________
(Please print or type)

Street Address ____________
(Please **do not** use PO Box)

City ____________

State ______ Zip ____________

Daytime phone number (____) - ____________

Thank you for your order!